MW00578748

MARRIAGE PAIN

from the
library
of

Sheila P. Silva

RECOVERY
DISCOVERY

MARRIAGE PAIN

Developing New Patterns in Your Relationship

Randy Reynolds & David Lynn

ZondervanPublishingHouse
Grand Rapids, Michigan

A Division of HarperCollins*Publishers*

Marriage Pain
Copyright © 1992 by Randy Reynolds and David Lynn

Requests for information should be addressed to:
Zondervan Publishing House
Grand Rapids, Michigan 49530

ISBN 0-310-57291-6

All Scripture quotations, unless otherwise noted, are taken from the HOLY BIBLE: NEW INTERNATIONAL VERSION® (North American Edition). Copyright © 1973, 1978, 1984, by the International Bible Society. Used by permission of Zondervan Publishing House.

"NIV" and "New International Version" are registered in the United States Patent and Trademark Office by the International Bible Society.

All rights reserved. No part of this publication may be reproduced, stored in a retrieval system, or transmitted in any form or by any means—electronic, mechanical, photocopy, recording, or any other—except for brief quotations in printed reviews, without the prior permission of the publisher.

Edited by Linda Vanderzalm
Interior design by Ann Cherryman
Cover design by Lecy Design
Cover photo by Dan Hummel

Printed in the United States of America

92 93 94 95 96 97 / DP / 10 9 8 7 6 5 4 3 2 1

CONTENTS

Dedicated to Carol Evans, who has been a great support to me and who was instrumental in helping me understand the loop.

Introduction

Many of us need to recover from the damage done by unhealthy marriage relationships, relationships marked by conflict, negative beliefs, and compulsive behavior patterns. Conflict in itself is not necessarily negative. But when conflict is unresolved, it often turns into a power struggle, with each spouse needing to win.

Recovery from damaged marriages is similar to recovery from addictions: *denial* plays a central role in keeping people and relationships sick. As long as you deny your marriage has a problem, you will not recover. As long as you deny that you are just as responsible as your spouse is for your unhealthy marriage, you will not recover. The first step to wholeness is admitting you have a problem.

It's painful to look at your relationship and own up to your part of the mess. It's painful to look at your sinful behavior. But your willingness to acknowledge your sin and humble yourself is the first step to freedom.

This workbook will help you look at your marriage relationship and determine where you get stuck. You will examine unhealthy dynamics that contribute to negative feelings and rob you of the joy God intends for you. You will go through some basic processes that bring health and healing to marriage relationships. You will look at several key elements that are essential to a healthy relationship. You may discover why other things you have done to improve your marriage relationship haven't worked, why trying harder often makes things worse.

The brokenness in your marriage may be in part the result of dysfunction and brokenness in your background. Destructive cycles are generational; they are handed down from generation to generation. It may seem unfair to you that your alcoholic parent has contributed to the dysfunction of your marriage or that your spouse's parents have played a part in hurting your marriage.

In biblical terms dysfunction is nothing less than sin, and everyone is a sinner; we all fall short of God's ideal. The greater the sin, the more intense the damage and destruction. Coming to terms with that damage usually brings feelings of anger, grief, and loss. If you are willing to work through your feelings and work toward recovery, you may help break some of these destructive cycles in your life and hand down a healthier relationship to your children and their children.

It is painful to look at the problems in your marriage, but as you acknowledge them and submit them to God's healing grace, your marriage will improve. God delights in being a God of redemption, bringing good things out of bad situations and relationships. If you turn to him for help in your marriage, he will bless you.

Recovery is a process that takes time. It is not an event or a cure. It will cost you to work on your recovery. You will experience pain, but it will be worth the price.

We hope this Recovery Discovery workbook will help you in your recovery from your damaged marriage. Our goal in *Marriage Pain* is to give you information and hope so that you can get past your pain and move on. Each chapter consists of five sections. *Recovery Focus* highlights the issues the chapter will discuss. *Recovery Information* explains the issues with which you may be wrestling, while the *Recovery Probers* gives questions that help you take a personal look at your own place in the recovery process. The *Recovery Guide* is designed to help you explore Scripture passages that give perspective to the recovery issues and to point you to God as a source of wisdom and strength. At the end of each chapter, the *Recovery Goals* gives you a chance to formulate goals that you need to work on as you move toward wholeness and recovery.

Take the time to write out your answers to the questions in each chapter. Reflect carefully on your feelings and beliefs. Pray, asking God to use this workbook as a tool for your recovery. Then discuss your insights and feelings with someone—ideally with a small group that will study this workbook together.

If you are part of such a group, speak up. Share your thoughts with the group. Look to the others for help and support. Learn from them as they share their stories and struggles. Pray together, depending on God to work in your lives. And rejoice together as you grow and find wholeness in your recovery.

If you aren't able to be part of a small group, talk over your recovery process with a trusted pastor, counselor, or balanced and trustworthy friend. Share your responses and questions with that other person. Ask him or her to pray for you regularly.

We live in a society of instant solutions—instant oil changes for our cars, fast food for our on-the-go lifestyles, quick-fix solutions to economic and social problems, and rushed quiet times with God. But recovery is not instant. Rather, your recovery will be an exciting and lifelong adventure of growing closer to God, to others, and to yourself. Welcome to the journey.

1.   Your Marriage Type

RECOVERY FOCUS

- Examine the two types of power struggles.
- Determine your part in the power struggle.
- Learn to function in a win-win dynamic.

RECOVERY INFORMATION

Conflict is a normal part of married life. Husbands and wives disagree about a lot of things. Conflict in itself is not bad. It's what we do with conflict, how we handle conflict that can make it a destructive force in our marriage. And when the conflict continues unresolved in the form of a power struggle, it causes damage.

Some dominance and dependence is natural in a relationship. In some areas of life one spouse is dominant; in other areas the other spouse takes the lead. It's not the positions that cause problems as much as what occurs out of these positions.

A power struggle develops when one person tries to control or manipulate the other. It is a battle of who will win and who will lose. Power struggles cause a loss of team work, cooperation, and mutuality. Individual interests become more important than the relationship, and the relationship becomes oppositional.

Power struggles often take two forms: the win-lose struggle and the lose-lose struggle. Let's take a closer look at both patterns.

THE WIN-LOSE RELATIONSHIP

In the win-lose pattern of handling conflict, one person is dominant and the other is dependent. The dominant person uses some kind of power to force the other person to yield. The dominant person may use anger, criticism, punishment, being right, being responsible, being more rational, threats, lectures, verbal or physical abuse to get his or her way.

The dependent person, on the other hand, usually withholds what the other person wants. The dependent person withdraws, complains, or acts helpless, irresponsible, dumb, forgetful, tired, or sick. The dependent person may try to please the other person because he is afraid to express himself verbally in the relationship.

These games are not played on a conscious or premeditated level. They are gut-level *reactions* to the other person's behavior.

This dominant-dependent dynamic will not be consistent in every area of the relationship. In some areas the husband will be dominant and his wife dependent; in other areas the wife will be dominant and her husband will be dependent.

Fred and Jane got stuck in a win-lose power struggle. Fred, an easygoing man, was intimidated by Jane's anger and assertiveness. When Jane would get angry and yell, Fred would yield to placate Jane's anger, remembering ugly scenes from his childhood. "It's not worth the fight," Fred would say. "It only makes her more upset."

Fred's lack of responsiveness totally frustrated Jane. At first she felt Fred's yielding was positive. But she soon learned that Fred's yielding did not make him cooperative. In fact, he became increasingly resistant. He would simply withhold what Jane wanted. Jane may have won the external battle, but she lost the unity of the relationship.

Fred and Jane were locked in a power struggle in which neither would emerge a winner. Jane paid the price of looking like the evil witch by dominating. However, she felt her only options were to do everything herself or to make Fred do something by yelling at him. Fred tried to hide his frustration and anger. Although he appeared to be the good guy or the innocent party, he paid the price of looking like an abused but weak and impotent husband. Fred felt his only options were to withdraw and yield or escalate a conflict, which would "make everyone miserable."

THE LOSE-LOSE RELATIONSHIP

In the lose-lose pattern of handling conflict, both people are powerful and openly exert their power. The relationship focuses on reciprocity: "I will give if you give." The problem starts when spouses begin to mistrust each other and harbor resentments. They then spend much of the relationship sabotaging the other spouse. They both feel that they will never be able to satisfy the wants and demands of the other partner; enough will never be enough.

The power struggle begins when both spouses begin to lose in the relationship. A trading of evil for evil begins, a kind of tit for tat based on anger and resentment that is often beyond awareness. The "I will give if you give" turns into "If you don't give, I won't give."

George and Sarah had been married for a number of years and had their share of struggles. George loved sailing and flying and got very excited about sharing these activities with his wife. Sarah loved being at home and spending time with the children and her husband.

George would complain to others that Sarah was "no fun." He started to resent the time he spent with her and the children at home. His resentment ruined everyone's time. George usually slipped in a few cutting remarks and vented some of his frustration indirectly.

Sarah would do the same thing when she went sailing with George. She would complain about how dangerous sailing was and how they were ignoring the children. Or she would come up with reasons not to go at all. Both George and Sarah blamed the other for the misery and failure in their own lives and withheld from each other to get even. "I'm glad George is frustrated because he sure frustrates us most of the time," said Sarah with some bitterness in her voice. "He is so insensitive to others. Someone has to hold him in line. It might as well be me."

"I don't care if Sarah ever gets what she wants from me because she doesn't deserve much the way she treats me. She is too self-centered anyway. That doesn't mean I don't love her. I do, very much," said George. George felt justified in being a roadblock in Sarah's life because he felt she was a roadblock to him.

Both George and Sarah felt they were giving more than they were receiving in their marriage. They both had collected resentments and lost trust and now were using the resentments and alienation to sabotage the other's life. They both felt it was their job to keep the other one "in line" and to straighten out the other's weaknesses. However, they were actually contributing to each other's weaknesses.

George and Sarah didn't feel they had a bad marriage since they loved and cared for each other. But they often denied their resentful feelings toward each other in order to protect the marriage. Finally the struggle became too miserable, and they admitted they had a love-hate relationship. They eventually went to counseling for help.

THE HEALTHY ALTERNATIVE:
THE WIN-WIN RELATIONSHIP

The mark of a healthy marriage is a sense of cooperation and mutuality, of trust and respect. We call this pattern the win-win relationship. The win-win relationship takes time and maturity to develop. It takes a commitment to respect the other person and to become a trustworthy partner.

Couples must be willing to give up the *reactivity* they use to protect themselves and become *pro-active* in creating this model in their relationship. Let us explain what we mean by reactivity and pro-activity. Reactivity is the unconscious, uncontrolled reaction to situations and other people's behavior. Pro-activity is intentional behavior aimed at a specific goal. So much of the negative behavior in power struggles is reactive, said and done without thinking. In order to break that pattern, you need to be willing to think through your behavior and act intentionally and for the purpose of building up your marriage.

Moving from reactivity to pro-activity takes maturity—the maturity to be honest with yourself and God, to see yourself and how you contribute to the power struggle. It takes the maturity to admit your mistakes and then to take risks, to be honest with your spouse about how he or she affects you and risk a conflict with him or her. This is often hard if you are a person who wants to keep peace.

As your marriage atmosphere changes from tension to relaxation, from distance to closeness, from hostility to warmth, the win-win dynamic begins to develop. Your relationship gains a feeling of goodwill and cooperation, a sense of freedom that gives acceptance and allows space. You find yourself committed to your spouse's well-being and needs. You find yourself working on the same team.

John and Dee had struggled in a win-lose power struggle for many years. John had a tendency to dominate in certain areas, and Dee was yielding but passive-aggressive, saying "yes" to John's suggestions but then not following through, thus frustrating John. John would often demand things, even when he was trying to be congenial. Dee would usually withhold things, even when her intentions were to cooperate.

After they had been in counseling for several months, John and Dee had a conversation they realized was not reactive and explosive. For the first time in years, they had made a healthy connection through their communication.

They were going out for the evening. John was ready, and Dee was late again—a ready formula for conflict between the two of them.

John: "Dee, are you doing this to frustrate me? We're going to be late again. Hurry up!"

Dee: "I'm hurrying as fast as I can. Have you seen my makeup?"

John: (Aware that he is getting frustrated, John wants to blow up and pressure Dee. Instead, he disengages.) "I'm going in the other room for a few minutes." (John prays and surrenders his right to be on time to God.)

Dee: (Appears in a few minutes.) "Thanks for giving me the space to get ready. That was the first time I felt you weren't pressuring me when we have been late. To be honest, sometimes I do go slower when you are pressuring me because I'm nervous and angry. I'm sorry about frustrating you and making you late."

John: "Dee, I do get very anxious when we are late to things."

Dee: "Oh, really?" (They both laugh.) "I'm willing to work on being on time, but what I need from you is some help with the kids and some space."

John: "That's what I tried to do tonight."

Dee: "I know, and it helped. Thanks."

John: "You're welcome."

John and Dee felt they had disengaged from their power struggle and were starting to cooperate in their marriage for the first time in a long while. Both felt that the other one cared and was investing in his or her interests. John and Dee were moving toward a win-win relationship.

CHOOSE THE HEALTHY ALTERNATIVE

You can have a win-win relationship. You can move from taking oppositional roles to working on the same team. Taking three important steps will help you break the power struggle and establish a win-win pattern of handling conflict: disengage, discover, and reveal.

Disengage. The first step is to disengage from the struggle. Learn to recognize your reactive patterns. Make a commitment to stop your reactions. Then disengage and stand back emotionally from the tug of war. If you do not disengage, fear or anger will control your responses and escalate the struggle.

You may find that you can disengage by biting your tongue and leaving the scene of the conflict for a period of time, as John did. Or you may find praying about your inner conflict will help. In some way, give yourself and your spouse some space to cool down and gather your emotions. Remember, it takes time, self-control, maturity, and practice to disengage and reduce the emotional reactivity.

Discover. The second step is to discover what your spouse thinks, feels, and wants. Once you have disengaged, try to see the situation through your spouse's eyes. You may presume to know what your spouse feels. But often that is part of the problem.

Commit yourself to taking the time to listen and show interest in your spouse's point of reference. Ask questions that show your spouse you care about his or her perspective, feelings, and desires. Find ways you can meet your spouse's needs and your own at the same time. Look for ways to cooperate and work together.

Reveal. Once you have listened, take the risk and reveal your own thoughts and feelings. Try to help your spouse understand your motives and desires. Remember, your goal is not to convince your spouse of the rightness of your point of view; that's back to a win-lose pattern. Your goal is to reveal yourself so that you can both work together.

RECOVERY PROBERS

1. How did your parents resolve conflict?

2. What role did your mother take? What role did your father take?

3. Are you more like your mother or father in dealing with conflict?

4. In which role do you see yourself most often, dominant or dependent?

5. Do you ever find yourself in the opposite role? When?

6. Do you try to control your spouse? How can you give up that control and turn it over to God?

7. How do you feel when you get into a power struggle with your spouse (example: angry, fearful)?

8. How do you disengage from the power struggle?

9. What do you need from God and your spouse to move toward a win-win pattern of handling conflict?

RECOVERY GUIDE

Read 2 Timothy 2:23–26.

1. Are you able to *not* react when someone opposes you?

2. What is your motive in quarreling with your spouse?

3. How can you "gently instruct" when you and your spouse are in a confrontation?

4. Who is responsible—you or God—to change your spouse's mind?

Read Proverbs 15:18.

1. Do you "stir up dissension" or "calm a quarrel"? Give an example.

2. What specific actions or words escalate your power struggles?

3. What can you do to work through your differences in a healthy way?

Read Proverbs 17:14.

1. How do your quarrels get out of control?

2. What is the difference between a discussion or negotiation and a quarrel?

Read Proverbs 18:2.

1. In what ways are you a good listener?

2. In what ways are you a poor listener?

3. Do others feel you understand them? If yes, how do you know?

RECOVERY GOALS

1. How would you describe your pattern of handling conflict in your marriage (win-lose, lose-lose, or win-win)? Explain.

2. What steps are you willing to take to make your marriage a healthier one?

3. What do you need to do to disengage from reactivity in your relationship?

4. What do you need to do to discover more about your spouse's point of view and feelings?

5. What do you need to reveal to your spouse so that he or she will understand you better?

2. Getting Your Marriage Unstuck

RECOVERY FOCUS

- Recognize your part in the reactionary loop in your marriage.
- Learn how you can break the reactionary loop.
- Choose to surrender your desires to God and stop the reaction.

RECOVERY INFORMATION

Once the battle for control settles into a marriage and a power struggle begins, a destructive cycle is in play. This cycle can be broken, but it's not easy. The more stress you have in your marriage and the more dysfunction you experienced in your childhood home, the more intense the cycle.

The cycle starts with feelings of needing to control. As a person begins to act on those feelings, both members of the relationship experience negative feelings. Those feelings may be fear, anger, mistrust, jealousy, sadness, guilt, inadequacy, as well as others. Honesty and openness are replaced by mistrust and deceit. These feelings then lead to negative behaviors, where couples begin to trade what the Bible calls "evil for evil." This in turn leads to negative judgments and the loss of trust, respect, and intimacy. The final outcome, if these negative cycles run their course, can be the loss of the relationship altogether.

Most often these cycles do not ruin the relationship completely. They just produce emotional distance and mistrust.

THE REACTIONARY LOOP

When you feel stuck, you often clearly see what your spouse could or should do to fix the situation. But it's hard for you to see what you can do. Your relationship is in a cycle, a cycle caused by both of you emotionally reacting to each other. We call this a *reactionary loop*.

The types and areas of loops are too numerous to mention, but let's look at a reactionary loop John and Dee fell into. Notice how the loop produces a polarization of roles in their marriage.

When John and Dee got married, the pastor spoke to them from Genesis 2:24, which says, "For this reason a man will leave his father and mother and be united to his wife, and they will become one flesh." The pastor said this meant that John and Dee's relationship was to take precedence over all other human relationships. Producing unity was not something that was going to be easy for them to accomplish.

John and Dee's loop began with a pursuer-distancer dynamic. John, a somewhat grumpy, demanding man, tended to be emotionally distant from Dee and the children. Dee, on the other hand, was friendly and emotionally available to her family. But her need to feel close often made John and the children feel engulfed by her.

This dynamic set the stage for their reactionary loop. When Dee pursued John for closeness, he felt swallowed and distanced from her. Dee wanted the closeness that the pastor had mentioned in the wedding ceremony but continually found herself hurt over the rejection and distance. John would feel angry at Dee's invasion into his space, which only made Dee more desperate to pursue closeness.

As the kids came along, Dee found she was able to feel safer and closer to the children. She naturally gravitated in their direction. This began a second loop in the relationship. John would feel left out, ganged up on, or lonely and would attack one or all of the children. John soon became the bad guy with the kids. When John attacked the children, Dee would side with them and comfort them emotionally. Dee became more and more the good guy. John then felt even more alienated and spent more time away from the family. Dee tried to compensate for John's behavior with the children by moving closer to them, which, of course, moved her further away from John.

As the loop increased in tension, the distance between John and Dee grew. John was polarizing in his role as the distancer and the bad guy, and Dee was polarizing in her role as the pursuer and the good guy. Both of them felt stuck and could not see how to get out of the roles they were in. They were losing their ability to work on the same team. They were losing each other as best friends and primary allies.

The loop in a marriage becomes more and more intense as each person reacts and becomes more entrenched in his or her role. Picture your hands held together with a rubber band. As you begin to spread your hands apart, or as they polarize, the movement creates so much tension that the rubber band breaks. This is how the loop works in a marriage. The increased tension of the loop makes relating unsafe and uncomfortable. Dee may feel that she has no other choice but to pursue John if she wants a relationship, "since he doesn't put anything into the relationship." However, Dee's *solution* to the problem becomes *part* of the problem, because John reacts to her pursuing by distancing. Dee feels that if she stopped pursuing, John would be relieved and would never initiate on his own. She feels she would lose him completely.

THE DYNAMICS OF OTHER LOOPS

You may recognize yourself in John and Dee's story. Or you may see yourself in one of these loops:

● She demands or engulfs by wanting him to be more responsible. She reacts by becoming more responsible and then resenting him more for withholding. He withholds acting responsibly because he resents that he is never good enough for her. He wants or passively demands that she relax. He reacts by minimizing the importance of the task, which only drives her back to becoming more responsible.

● He demands or engulfs by wanting sex from her. She is afraid of his demands and withholds sex. He reacts by becoming more passionate. She feels he is "only interested in sex." She reacts by becoming what he feels is "cold and frigid." The frustration builds.

● She wants him to be more spiritual, and when she feels he is not spiritual enough, she reacts by quoting Bible verses to him and trying to be more pious. He feels her piety and spirituality are out of touch with reality and phoney. He wants a bit more humanness and reacts by being human or maybe a little crass. She is threatened by this and heightens her spirituality.

● He wants her to be more strict with the children and reacts to her "permissiveness" by becoming stricter. She demands that he be more merciful and kind and reacts to his "authoritarian discipline" by becoming more lenient.

● She demands that he be more outgoing, verbal, affectionate, and social. He needs more quiet, peace, and space. He reacts to her demands by withdrawing. She reacts to his withholding by becoming more outgoing and engulfing. The loop is established, and both people begin to move further apart, polarizing in their roles.

BREAKING THE LOOP

Two dynamics empower these negative loops. First, you feel entitled to your position. You feel justified in desiring a close relationship, for instance, so you press to meet that goal. Second, when your spouse resists what you feel is your right, you feel hurt and resentful. You then feel "entitled" to respond with invasive, disrespectful, degrading, or vindictive behavior. You may even know on some level that your reaction is wrong, but you feel justified because of what your spouse is or is not doing in the loop.

Often this negative entitlement is verbalized as blame, complaining, or criticism. You focus on your spouse's part of the loop and overlook your own negative contribution. As your negative reaction intensifies, you become less and less able to love your spouse or accept your spouse for who he or she is. Your actions communicate, "If you change, I'll be happy. My happiness depends on your ability to change and meet my expectations." You may become deaf to the needs your spouse is expressing. Therefore you may appear very insensitive and withholding to your spouse.

Breaking the loop means you have to own your part of the destruction of the relationship and choose to change your behavior. It means you need to give up your entitlement and your resentments in order to be free. You must choose to stop justifying your negative behavior, even if your spouse's behavior doesn't change.

The steps in breaking the loop are similar to the first three steps in a twelve-step recovery program like the one used in Alcoholics Anonymous. Step one: Admit your reactions are out of control. Step two: Admit you need God's help to change. Step three: Turn your reactions and "rights" over to God, asking for his help in breaking the loop.

RECOVERY PROBERS

1. What reactionary loops do you recognize in your marriage?

2. What do you want or demand from your spouse?

3. How do you react when your spouse doesn't meet those wants or demands?

4. What role are you in and how is the polarization process making you into someone you do not want to be (examples: bad guy, frigid woman, alienated from important others, distancer)?

5. What are you afraid will happen if you quit reacting in the loop (example: He will become more authoritarian, and no one will be there to protect the children)?

6. What would you have to let go of in order to get out of the loop? (This is often a legitimate desire, such as sex, healthy children, a responsible spouse, etc.)

7. Why is trusting and turning to God important in breaking the loop?

8. If you own or take responsibility for your part of the loop and quit trying to change or resist your spouse, what will happen?

RECOVERY GUIDE
Read 1 John 1:7–9.
1. What is your area of sin in your reactionary loop?

2. What happens when you deny your own sin?

3. What will happen if you confess or own your sin?

4. Are you willing to take responsibility for that sinful behavior?

5. How does sin break fellowship?

Read Ephesians 4:25–27.

1. How are you phoney or false with your spouse?

2. Why are you often not honest with him or her?

3. Are you afraid to show your anger to your spouse? Why?

Read Romans 2:1–4.

1. In what ways do you pass judgment on your spouse?

2. In what ways are you disrespectful of your spouse?

3. According to this passage, what leads you toward repentance?

4. How do you feel when you are judged?

RECOVERY GOALS

1. Do you withhold or demand in your marriage? Explain.

2. How do you justify your behavior?

3. What steps are you willing to take to break the reactionary loop in your marriage?

4. What specific resentments and judgments are you willing to give up?

5. What specific desires will you place in God's hands?

6. The reactionary loop in your marriage will not be broken quickly. What will you do to keep patient and hopeful as you wait for God to work? Whose help will you enlist?

3.

Making Deposits in Your Marriage

RECOVERY FOCUS

- Refuse to return evil for evil.
- Make positive deposits in your marriage.
- Create a new loop.

RECOVERY INFORMATION

Human love is based on reciprocity. We need some kind of payback to keep motivated in most of our relationships. If a marriage includes a positive, balanced give and take, the relationship grows. However, if one spouse gives and the other only takes—without giving anything back—the relationship soon deteriorates.

If you feel that your relationship is marked by this kind of imbalance, you may feel cheated. Your sense of justice has been disturbed. You may feel that because you contribute to your marriage relationship, your spouse owes you.

AN EYE FOR AN EYE

Once this dynamic begins, your relationship may quickly deteriorate into the kind of reactionary loop we examined in the last chapter: You resent your spouse's treatment of you, and you react with behavior that only contributes to the negative loop. Because you feel you are being treated unfairly, you feel justified in being disrespectful or disloyal to your spouse. Or you may feel entitled to withhold your love from your spouse. You feel hurt because your needs are discounted or neglected. You collect unfairness, and you lose your motivation to love. The reactionary loop widens, and your relationship loses its warmth and affection.

As you give yourself permission to get even with your spouse, you may punish your spouse directly or indirectly. Direct retribution may involve venting your anger, calling your spouse names, judging your spouse's motives, making demands, or using verbal or physical violence. Indirect retribution may involve withholding from your spouse, minimizing or discounting your spouse's needs, or appeasing your spouse without changing your behavior. Your relationship is reduced to an eye-for-an-eye reactionary loop.

CREATING A NEW LOOP

In the last chapter we suggested that you could break the reactionary loop in your marriage by admitting that your reactions are out of control and by submitting your desires to God, trusting that with his help you can stop the negative reactivity. A second way to break the reactionary loop is to create a new, positive loop. Let us explain what we mean by creating a new loop.

In chapter 1 we explained the difference between reactivity and pro-activity. "Reactivity is the unconscious, uncontrolled reaction to situations and other people's behavior. Pro-activity is intentional, controlled behavior aimed at a specific goal." The reactionary loop is created by uncontrolled reactions. The new, positive loop is created by intentional, controlled behavior aimed at bringing unity and harmony back to the relationship.

Creating a new loop is a conscious, planned activity. It involves breaking the old behavior patterns by replacing them with new patterns.

Think of it this way. Each time you choose to behave in a way that leads toward harmony and unity, you are making a deposit in your marriage. You are investing in the future. You are investing in the building of a new, solid, harmonious relationship.

After months of counseling, John and Dee began making positive deposits into their marriage. In one of their counseling sessions, John, who usually only wanted to blame Dee, said, "I've been doing better because Dee is paying attention to me and respecting me."

"Well, it's easy to pay attention when you stay and talk things out rather than leave or yell," said Dee.

Both John and Dee were contributing to building a positive loop in their relationship. Many of their negative loops had been broken, and they were starting to replace them with positive ones. They each felt the effects of the other's efforts and were responsive to them. Investing in the relationship is essential to making it work. Like anything that must be built and maintained, relationships take risk, creativity, initiative, sensitivity, and contribution.

Part of building a positive relationship is acknowledging the efforts of your spouse and rewarding them. Often in deteriorating relationships, your communication is so poor that you can't see where your spouse is making sacrifices for you. You are out of touch with each other. You must be able to hear your spouse and discover how to balance the burdens and blessings he or she is experiencing.

John had almost always overlooked how Dee had put so much energy into the children. She had been carrying most of the burden of caring for them through the years. John began to share this responsibility and bring some balance to the task of parenting. He also told Dee what a great job she had done rather than attack her and the children. Dee felt great relief. Affection and trust were beginning to move her heart.

If one spouse feels he or she is carrying most of the load of the relationship, resentment builds. When each spouse cares about the burdens the other person is experiencing, the load becomes much lighter and injustices are less likely to be collected. When a spouse's efforts are rewarded through appreciation or acknowledgment, the relationship becomes enjoyable. Although it's hard to give when your contribution is taken for granted or criticized, it's easy when your spouse responds to your contribution in a favorable way. It takes maturity and turning to God to be able to create a relationship with a positive loop.

John and Dee realized that gaining what they wanted in their relationship involved a paradox: Before your needs can be met, you must first of all be concerned about meeting your spouse's needs. As you make positive deposits into your marriage, your spouse is freer to love you and meet your needs. That is very difficult when you feel your spouse is taking advantage of you.

Dee would feel resentful when John distanced himself and in reaction would either pursue him or ally with the kids. As she grew, she began to see John's distancing as a need. She could see that she could contribute by giving him the space he needed. John's positive reaction to that was that he felt cared for. He then needed less space and made greater efforts at moving closer to Dee. This contributed to both of them investing more in a good relationship. And as John matured and relied more on God, he was less dependent on Dee's goodwill. He found that he could initiate closeness even when he felt she was not giving him the space he needed.

Both John and Dee felt their relationship was building up stock in the areas of trust and affection. They were creating a positive loop.

RECOVERY PROBERS

1. In what area do you feel your spouse is not reciprocating?

2. How do you feel about that?

3. What is your reaction? Do you withhold or demand?

4. Is it difficult for you to trust God in this area? Why?

5. Are you being honest and making requests of your spouse?

6. What do you need in order to be able to trust your spouse? Write it out and define it specifically.

7. Where can you make a positive contribution and begin to reverse the loop (example: If you normally withhold, begin to contribute; if you normally hurt or demand, back off and show respect)?

8. What unfinished business from your childhood family do you bring into your marriage?

9. Are you expecting your spouse to react or treat you as your parent(s) did?

10. How is your role in your childhood family contributing to the problems in your marriage? (For more information about this issue, see *Family Pain: Healing for Adult Children of Alcoholic and Other Dysfunctional Families*, part of this Recovery Discovery series.)

11. How can you begin creating a new, positive loop in your marriage?

RECOVERY GUIDE

Before you can make a positive contribution in your relationship, you must give up your resentments and anger toward your spouse. Perhaps you will need to go back a generation and give up your bitterness toward a parent before you will be able to forgive your spouse. Before you can be free to receive again, you must first forgive the offense before God. If you are full of anger and resentment, you will not be able to give or receive positive contributions. Your resentment will lead you to look for an underlying motive and discount your spouse's contribution. Your spouse will feel discouraged and have a difficult time contributing, which will only continue the negative loop. The solution is forgiveness.

Read Ephesians 4:29–32.

1. What are the contrasting concepts in these verses?

2. How do they relate to the negative and positive loops?

3. How does this relate to you?

Read Hebrews 12:14—15.
1. What does it mean to "live in peace" with your spouse?

2. How can you miss the grace of God?

3. In what ways are you missing God's grace in your marriage relationship?

Read Romans 14:19.
1. What does it mean to "edify" someone?

2. What effort can you make to edify your spouse?

3. When and how will you do this?

RECOVERY GOALS

1. What are your spouse's most pressing needs?

2. What deposits will you make to meet those needs?

4. Dealing with Your Desires

RECOVERY FOCUS

- Recognize where you and your spouse are stuck in your marriage.
- Choose to surrender your desires to God.
- Give your spouse the gift of safety.

RECOVERY INFORMATION

One of the important goals of marriage is intimacy, being able to share deeply personal and meaningful things with another person who cares about you. Why, then, is it often difficult to share your most personal issues with your spouse?

Every marriage has an agenda. You got married for a reason; you desire or expect certain things. Many times these desires are legitimate: wanting to have children, desiring healthy children, wanting closeness, attention, romance, help, sex, order around the house, financial security, cooperation, respect, encouragement, freedom to succeed, space, to be held in high esteem, or to be able to talk things through.

You feel you have the right to expect your spouse to fill these desires. When your expectations aren't met, you may feel hurt or disappointed. You may find yourself becoming distant or unusually demanding in your marriage. You feel stuck and don't know what to do.

You try to talk with your spouse about your unmet expectations, but he or she is unable to talk about it. Your spouse may see your need as a threat or as something about which he or she can do nothing. Your spouse may be irritated with you for having needs and may express only helplessness and hopelessness.

Your marriage has reached an impasse. You are stuck.

You may feel like a scuba diver who has run out of oxygen. You know your diving companion, your spouse, has more oxygen in his or her tank, but you can't seem to communicate that you need to share the tank. You motion to your spouse. You try to indicate that you're desperate for oxygen, but he or she doesn't understand or is unwilling to share the oxygen. You feel as if you are going to die. You cling on to your spouse, grabbing the oxygen tube. Confused and irritated, your spouse only fights you and swims away.

If your unfulfilled desire is basic to your sense of security, you may feel desperate, like the scuba diver. You may try to engulf or control your spouse in order to have your need met. You may not realize how your intensity affects your spouse, especially if your focus is on what you feel are legitimate desires.

However, sometimes your spouse doesn't understand what you want or can't give you what you want or can't give you enough of what you want to satisfy you. Your spouse may feel threatened and may feel inadequate to satisfy your "insatiable" appetite. Your spouse may resent the continued demand, feeling you are unappreciative of the sacrifices and contributions he or she makes to you. This results in an impasse.

You may feel afraid to express your desire because you don't want to feel frustrated again. To protect yourself from further hurt, you may resort to judgmental or critical attitudes: "He doesn't care. He's too selfish." "She is just a cold woman like her mother." These judgments may have truth in them, but they focus on the worst in the other person and serve the purpose of self-protection.

Once this point is reached, dialogue and intimacy are gone in a relationship. Often this is the point at which spouses begin to head out of the relationship to get their "legitimate desires" met elsewhere.

Both John and Dee had legitimate sexual desires. All Dee wanted was for John to listen to her and value her. That was a legitimate desire, wasn't it? All John wanted was to have a wife who was attracted to him. That was a legitimate desire, wasn't it?

Dee wanted John to initiate time with her and be interested and responsive to her feelings. When he didn't initiate and she had to ask him for that time, it was spoiled for her. She felt John was paying attention to her only because she asked, not because he really was interested in her. Dee then felt stuck and didn't know what to do. If she didn't say anything, he remained distant, and she felt abandoned and hurt. If she asked and he gave a half-hearted effort, she was frustrated and became furious. She found that as the relationship progressed, she resorted to desperate behavior to get John's attention.

She would yell at him and call him names. This only led her to feel worse about herself.

John also had struggles. He was very attracted to Dee. He would initiate physical intimacy and hope she felt the same way. Usually she was not responsive to his initiations but eventually gave in to satisfy him. John felt their sex life was not very rewarding. He would try not to be sexually needy, but then he would feel frustrated and find himself acting out in ways that brought him shame. He would then get angry at Dee for not being more sexually responsive.

At times, John would become more romantic. When that didn't work, he would get angry and call Dee frigid or cold. He would then apologize and withdraw, feeling guilty. John was so frustrated that he wished he would not have any sexual desires, but he also felt marriage was the right place to be able to express his sexual desires.

John began to distance emotionally, feeling engulfed by Dee's desire for emotional closeness. He was withholding from her without realizing how it would affect the relationship. Dee began withholding sex from John because she felt unloved. She felt if John would be nurturing, she would be able to respond to him sexually. However, she did not tell him this because they could no longer talk without quickly reaching an impasse.

These impasses left them both feeling frustrated and impotent. They were stuck without intimacy, both verbal and sexual. The relationship was no longer a safe place for them, and they were losing hope that they would ever get their legitimate desires met. How could this impasse be broken?

CREATING A SAFE PLACE

To break the impasse, both you and your spouse need to focus on your own issues rather than on the inadequacy of your spouse. And the first step in that process is *to surrender your desires to God*. This is one of the mysteries of the Christian faith: surrender brings freedom; dying to your desires brings life and fulfillment.

When you surrender your desires to God, he works his will in his way and his time. You must take your hands off the process and wait. That means you quit demanding and blaming your spouse. You stop punishing your spouse, and you give him or her space.

In terms of the scuba-diving metaphor, surrender means stop trying to get your spouse to share his or her tank. Swim to the surface of the water and get your own oxygen tank replaced or refilled at the boat. As you do this, you take the pressure off your spouse. You eliminate the confusion and fear he or she may be feeling because of your desperate, demanding behavior.

As you surrender your needs to God and trust him to fill them, you will find that your power struggle will subside because the real issue is not between you and your spouse but between you and God. As you turn to God, your heart will begin to change. You may find that your need for security will be met in ways you never expected. This frees up your relationship and makes the relationship safe. You and your spouse can resume your "scuba-diving activities" because you each have your own tank of oxygen.

When you surrender your demanding behavior to God, you give the gift of safety to your spouse. Your spouse is now free not only to say no when he or she is unable to respond to your needs but also to give wholeheartedly—not as a forced gesture to satisfy your unrelenting demands—when he or she is able to say yes. Your relationship will move from a win-lose or lose-lose struggle to a win-win dynamic.

On the other hand, if you are a withholder, surrendering to God will enable you to overcome your fears. You will be able to say no to your demanding spouse when you need to, and you will be able to say yes—and act on that yes—when you want to. As a result, the demander will no longer feel abandoned or cheated, for you will have become a contributor.

This will result in a feeling of connectedness and closeness for both you and your spouse. The impasse will be broken. Now both of you can come out and play because the relationship is safe again. As you give your needs to God, conversation will be easier and intimacy will develop. Making safety a goal for the other person breaks the impasse.

RECOVERY PROBERS

1. **What are your expectations of your marriage relationship? What is your agenda?**

2. **What desires do you feel are not met in your marriage? What is the oxygen you feel you desperately need?**

3. In what ways are you too dependent on your spouse for your happiness?

4. How do you feel when you get stuck in an impasse?

5. Do you feel selfish about your desires in your marriage relationship? How?

6. What desires do you need to surrender to God?

7. How can God replace or refill your empty oxygen tank?

8. How do you know you can trust God with your needs?

9. How does God make us die to our hopes and desires before he restores them? Describe a personal or biblical example of a time when this happened.

10. In what areas of your relationship do you have a difficult time talking honestly and openly?

11. What can you do to make it safe for your spouse to talk about his or her desires and concerns in your relationship?

12. How does becoming more independent take pressure off a reactive relationship?

RECOVERY GUIDE

The Bible is full of stories of people who surrendered their desires to God only to find that God fulfilled those desires in amazing and surprising ways. God did not act immediately in every situation; in fact, many of the people had to wait through difficult circumstances before they saw God's answer. But in each case, God fulfilled the desire in a way more rich and complete than the person would have imagined.

Moses wanted to deliver his people from Egyptian slavery when he was a powerful Egyptian prince, but he was rejected as a leader. Then as a humble shepherd, he was called to be one of the most powerful leaders of all time, and his desire was fulfilled.

Joseph expected to be a leader in his family but instead became a slave. Then from a prison cell he was called to be a leader over all of Egypt.

Abraham wanted a son, but his wife was barren. After waiting for many years, Abraham finally received God's fulfillment in Isaac, the son of God's promise.

Read 2 Corinthians 4:10–11.

1. How is surrender like a death experience?

2. What is on the other side of surrender? How does that help you in the surrendering process?

3. One of the most difficult things to give up is self-protection, which we maintain through judgmental attitudes and critical spirits. If you know that God will protect and provide, how does that help in the surrender process?

Read Matthew 7:7-8.

1. Do you trust God with your needs?

2. For what do you need to ask God?

3. What risks do you need to take?

4. Where do you need to turn your attention?

Read Psalm 18:2.

1. In what ways is God your protection?

2. Do you doubt his ability to protect you? Can you be honest with him about your doubt?

3. Is it okay to ask God to show you his protection and provision?

4. Does God want to reveal himself to you?

RECOVERY GOALS

Intimacy in a relationship requires safety. To have safety, both members of the relationship must look at themselves first, working through their own personal issues before they can make the relationship safe for the other person.

1. **What steps will you take to make your marriage relationship a safe place?**

2. **What desires will you place in God's hands?**

3. **How long are you willing to wait for God to act?**

4. **How will you maintain hope in God as you wait?**

5. **If you are withholding, when will you be ready to contribute?**

5. Alliances That Hurt Your Marriage

RECOVERY FOCUS

- Realize how you bring other alliances into your marriage.
- Change alliances that hinder your alliance with your spouse.
- Develop a strong primary alliance with your spouse.

RECOVERY INFORMATION

In whom do you confide when you feel insecure or are facing stress? Who gives you comfort and a sense of safety? This person is your *primary ally*.

A primary ally is your main loyalty, next to God. This is someone you can trust and who is there for you. For some people, especially those who distance, their primary ally may not be a person: It may be work, self, television, or some other thing.

One of the goals of marriage is teamwork, an alliance of two people working together to fight the world. Many times in marriages that are not functioning well, it takes a long time and a lot of work for this primary alliance to develop. In the best marriages it takes time. When an impasse shows up in a marriage, a primary alliance may also shift to someone or something else.

SECURITY AND ESTEEM IN ALLIANCES

When trust has broken down and a marriage relationship faces an impasse, spouses often go outside of the relationship to get their basic needs met. Dr. Larry Crabb, in his book *The Marriage Builder*, says our basic needs are for *security* and *significance*.

Some marriages never really bond because the spouses have never become primary allies for each other. They have not become a source of security and self-esteem, or at least not the primary source. This is what some psychologists call a "failure to leave home." Even though the spouse has physically left home, he or she is still emotionally entangled. This hinders the bonding in the marriage relationship. Often these other alliances threaten the marriage, making one of the spouses feel something is not right because God ordained that the primary loyalty should be to one's spouse.

When a spouse becomes impatient and attacks the other spouse's source of security and significance, it usually weakens the marriage relationship and strengthens the other alliance. ("Your mother always has her nose in our business, and you are too dependent on her." "Your work is constantly taking time away from our relationship. I don't know why you can't get things done.")

Recovery means that you can be honest and talk about your feelings, but it does not mean you create another demand-withhold loop. It means that together you are able to set up boundaries that protect the marriage relationship. It also means you become a better ally by learning to meet your spouse's basic needs.

John and Dee both had alliances that seemed to hinder their bonding with each other. However, these alliances also seemed to stabilize their relationship when they were having their worst fights. Dee felt that John often ignored her feelings and was hurt by his callous approach to problem solving. When she felt hurt, she found talking to her mother was a great comfort to her. Her mother was always encouraging and did not take sides. Dee always felt better after talking to her mom and could deal a little better with John's reactive behavior.

John, however, felt jealous of Dee's mother and at times resented their relationship. He would feel left out when she spent time with her mother and complain, "You seem to enjoy your mother more than me." The truth was that Dee did enjoy spending time with her mother more than with John. However, she didn't have the courage to tell John the truth.

Dee's attempt to protect John's feelings was not helpful to the relationship. It kept them stuck. She felt guilty because she tried hard to make John a priority. Dee also enjoyed her time with the children and her friends more than her time with John. John and Dee did not really enjoy each other.

John also had alliances that hurt his marriage. When he felt uncomfortable, he would not talk about it. Instead, he buried himself in his work. Work was one of the few places that made him feel good.

Through his work, John felt he was showing his parents that he could make it. John was proud of his work.

Dee, however, was not proud of John's work, feeling that it often was a distraction from the family. John saw his work as a valuable contribution to the family's financial stability and saw Dee's criticism as a lack of support and gratitude.

Several times when Dee and John had fought about John's attention to work, John had gone to talk to his mother, who would encourage him and tell him what a good provider he was. After talking to his mother, John would feel good about himself and his work.

Both John and Dee put a lot of energy into alliances outside their marriage relationship, venting feelings of anxiety, anger, and inadequacy. Although John and Dee would feel better after they had talked with their other alliances, it left them with no resolve between them.

Their marriage relationship at times needed the outside support, but the support also seemed to keep them from resolving the problems between the two of them. John and Dee sometimes found more intimacy and safety in their other alliances than in their marriage. Both John and Dee were able to say to other people things they couldn't tell each other. Why? They lacked the courage and self-control to talk things out with each other, to confront the other face to face, and to value the other enough to listen without reacting.

CAN WE TALK?

When you have experienced negative loops and impasses in your marriage, you may find it scary to approach touchy subjects. Your fear keeps you from forming a strong, primary alliance with your spouse. Fear is a negative belief that has often been formed from bad experiences in the marriage. You feel your spouse will never change. You feel your spouse will only react negatively if you try to talk about your real feelings.

The antidote to fear is faith. You must take risks in areas where you have desires. But, you may ask, won't this just create another loop? Faith is not you creating or making something happen; it's trusting that God will bring positive results as you do what you are supposed to do. You must keep God in the center of your marriage to keep the loop from appearing again. Let him bring the results, in his time, in his way.

Faith moves you away from your fears and helps you not be controlled or threatened by them. This in turn keeps you from power struggles or controlling behavior, whether that be withholding or demanding. This faith can give you the courage to let go of your fears and start opening up lines of true communication. This will help rebuild trust and build an alliance.

Both John and Dee had plenty of fears toward each other. Dee was often paralyzed by John's anger and found herself overwhelmed by fear. John often felt more inadequate or stupid when in an argument with Dee because of her verbal ability. He was intimidated and would find himself struggling. He felt anger was his main ally when pressured by her verbal intensity. Neither trusted the other, and they had many negative beliefs that kept them stuck.

As they worked through their reactionary loop, they found a void in their relationship. They were not fighting, but they also were not relating, because they were afraid of fighting. They just didn't believe they would ever relate well. This void needed to be replaced, or they would soon regress due to boredom.

Their counselor asked both John and Dee how they kept their fears and negative beliefs alive. John said, "Well, every time I see that old look in Dee's eye, I withdraw. I also talk to my mom about Dee. I don't mean to, but I just say negative things about Dee to her." John was keeping both his fears and negative beliefs about Dee alive through his relationship with his mother.

The counselor asked John if he would be willing to apologize to Dee for this gossip and tell his mother he would not be talking to her about Dee anymore. John agreed to stop his behavior if Dee would be willing to stop some of her alliances with her friends and her mother. Dee agreed to John's negotiations on the condition that John would not abandon her when they were attempting to work out their differences.

It actually took several months to move the alliances from outside the marriage to inside the marriage. Both John and Dee continued to attack the other's relationships rather than let the other person be responsible to do what was right. However, they did begin to see that they could rebuild trust through letting go of their fears and negative beliefs and through having faith and talking with each other.

RECOVERY PROBERS

1. In what ways is your marriage a primary alliance for you?

2. In what ways is your marriage a primary alliance for your spouse?

3. In what ways have you formed alliances that undermine your marriage relationship?

4. In what ways has your spouse formed alliances that undermine your marriage relationship?

5. What are the benefits of your other alliances?

6. What alliance would be the most difficult for you to let go of?

7. Do you feel safe and secure in your marriage?

8. What fears hinder your relationship to your spouse? Are you facing those fears?

9. How can you move toward a stronger alliance in your relationship with your spouse?

10. What scares you the most about moving closer to your spouse?

RECOVERY GUIDE
Read Ephesians 5:31.

1. How does knowing that God sees your marriage relationship as a primary alliance make a difference to you?

2. What does the phrase "will become" mean to you?

3. What does loyalty mean to you?

Read Psalm 20:7.

1. Why would a Jewish warrior trust in horses or chariots over God?

2. How can trusting in something that is helpful be a distraction or disloyalty?

3. What do you depend on or trust in more than God?

Read Hebrews 11:1.

1. How is faith the opposite of fear?

2. Is it scary for you to define what you want? Explain.

3. How does God produce faith in you?

4. In what areas do you lack faith?

RECOVERY GOALS

Deepening your relationship to God will strengthen your primary alliance with your spouse. God will come to each marriage partner, deal with your hearts, and allow more safety in the marriage. This can help the withholder to contribute and the demander to relax and wait. This puts the timing for recovery in God's hands and allows it to happen his way.

1. In what ways can you deepen your relationship to God?

2. How will this strengthen your alliance with your spouse?

3. What do you need to let go of before your alliance with your spouse can become stronger?

4. When would you be willing to let go of this?

5. What do you need in order to let go (examples: support, courage, help from spouse)?

6. What must you do to move closer to your spouse?

7. When would you be willing to start this?

6. Your Part in Reconciliation

RECOVERY FOCUS

- Choose to take the first step toward reconciliation.
- Acknowledge and confess how your sin affects your spouse.
- Focus on your trust in God.

RECOVERY INFORMATION

Reconciliation of a broken or damaged marriage relationship involves learning to forgive. If your spouse has hurt you, if your trust has been wounded, you may find it very difficult to reinvest in your marriage relationship. You may wonder how you can be loving to someone who has mistreated you or who withholds from you. You may wonder how you can forgive someone who continues to hurt you.

Ideally both marriage partners work together toward reconciliation. But what if your spouse is not at a point to work at your relationship? Do you wait until he or she is ready? Can you afford to wait that long?

You can choose to take the first step. You can work toward making your relationship a safe place. You can choose to work through your heart issues, whether or not your spouse is working on his or her issues. To *have* a dependable partner, you often have to *be* a dependable partner. This type of maturity can bring reconciliation in a relationship.

Maturity may mean that you demonstrate positive character qualities—humility, honesty, justice, mercy, patience—when your spouse continues to be selfish. This doesn't mean you are in a one-up position of being better than your spouse, and it doesn't mean that you deny your humanness. It also doesn't mean you have to be the only giver or ignore your spouse's part in the relationship. (If codependency is an issue for you, work through *Codependency Confusion: Developing*

Healthy Relationships, one of the workbooks in this Recovery Discovery series).

How do you begin to make your relationship a safe place? How can you take the first steps toward reconciliation?

The answer can be found in your relationship to God. When you feel wounded by your spouse, do you hold on to your anger or hurt to protect your heart from further wounds? When you do this, you also distance yourself from God by harboring the resentment or hurt. Sometimes you even blame God because you feel it's his fault for allowing this hurt in your life.

The first step to gaining safety in a relationship is to give your anger to God, asking him to soften your heart. Before you can expect your spouse to become involved in reconciliation, you must open yourself to God, allowing him to change you and develop character and maturity within you.

Dee had begun to see that what she was doing in her relationship with John was getting her nowhere. She felt stuck, not knowing what to do. John sometimes saw Dee as a self-righteous person and resented her arrogance. But he also respected her kindness and goodness. John also felt that Dee collected hurts and used them to stay distant.

Through counseling Dee began to see how her lack of forgiveness with John was keeping her distant from God, even though she was active in church and Bible study. She trusted God in many areas of her life, but she found it hard to trust God for change in her marriage; she had prayed many times for change in John's life, but nothing changed.

Dee decided to ask God to help her forgive John for the hurt he caused her and to release her from those hurts and resentments. As she did this, she began to trust God to protect her and gained a new peace in her heart. Dee had been using her faith to protect herself and keep herself distant from John by praying that God would change him. Now Dee was more open to having God change her and began to pray for guidance in her own life. God brought conviction to Dee's heart about how judgmental she was toward John. She also saw how she formed primary alliances with other people and cut off John emotionally.

As Dee saw her sinful behavior, she became more convinced that she needed to ask John's forgiveness. She took a risk and went to John, asking if he would forgive her for the ways her sinful behavior had contributed to their marriage problems. John said he was willing to forgive her and was glad she was aware of her negative behavior patterns. Then Dee asked John how her behavior made him feel. John jumped at the opportunity to share the effect that Dee had had on him. "I felt abandoned by you, like you didn't even want me. I was very hurt and angry with you and the kids. I always felt that you were better than I was and that your judgmental attitude put me there. I felt helpless and powerless around you when you did those things to me." John was angry and teary-eyed when he expressed that to Dee.

For the first time Dee did not feel defensive. She knew she was guilty of her behavior and that it had negatively affected John. In the past she might have said, "If you were not so angry and abrupt, I would not distance myself." There was no need to do this now. Dee just said, "John, would you forgive me for how my attitudes and behaviors have affected you? I was wrong and am truly sorry." John was elated and said he would forgive her for the effects of her sin. He felt Dee was finally going to be a wife to him.

A few days later John felt something was still wrong in the relationship. He started blaming Dee for distancing. Dee looked directly at John and said, "John, I love you, but I don't trust you." John immediately became angry and left for work. He had not worked through the process Dee had and was not sure he wanted to yet. Reconciliation was not complete because John had not completed his part. Dee felt some doubt about whether or not John would ever change.

TRUSTING GOD MEANS ALLOWING SPACE

Dee was now feeling vulnerable. Fear and doubt could move her to behavior that might start the loops going again. She had surrendered her marriage to God, but she was having a hard time waiting for him to bring the desired results. However, if Dee refused to give in to her doubts, she would do two positive things for herself and John: She would be growing in character and maturity, and she would be showing respect for John.

Change is a process that doesn't happen overnight or by magic just because you follow the right steps. Change happens as your heart changes and grows. Dee needed support to hold on to her faith. Her counseling sessions with John and her codependency support group helped her understand herself better and helped develop more trust in God.

When you trust God to change your relationship—starting with you—you need to allow time and space for the relationship to heal. God will work, but you need to trust his timing. If you become impatient or anxious, you may fall back into negative loops, and your spouse's attitude and behavior may get worse before they get better.

Change is scary. It's safer to stay with the familiar than to pursue something better. However, when you refuse to play the old games anymore, it's difficult for your spouse not to make some changes. True reconciliation takes time. It's not just admitting your wrongs but actually changing them to rights. This takes time and follow through. If your motive is to change your spouse rather than to allow God to change you first, your behavior change will be temporary. When the old patterns reappear, trust is lost again.

When you and your spouse can acknowledge how your behavior affects each other, you have taken an important step toward reconciliation. As you allow God to change your negative behavior, trust will build in the relationship.

What if you change, but your spouse doesn't? What if your spouse responds to your steps toward reconciliation with indifference? What if your spouse continues to mistreat you? Those are tough questions. Remember this: You need to be more concerned about yourself and your behavior, trusting God to take care of your spouse and your marriage relationship. Often when you focus on your relationship to God, other things fall in line. (If you are being victimized by your spouse's abuse, neglect, or addiction, you may need to find additional help from a codependency group, individual therapy, or a professional intervention.)

Recovery from a damaged marriage requires not only forgiveness but also repentance. Repentance is the complete change in direction that is essential for the rebuilding of trust in the relationship. Begin to care about how your behavior affects your spouse. Be willing to own up to negative behavior that causes problems, and make amends when you fall into old patterns. If you have been withholding from your spouse, repent from that behavior; acknowledge that your lack of love brings feelings of abandonment to your spouse, and resolve to change. If you are a demanding spouse, repent from that behavior; acknowledge that your demanding behavior shows a lack of love, causing discomfort and wounds in your spouse. Forgiveness and repentance are a normal process in recovering from damaged relationships.

RECOVERY PROBERS

1. **For what do you need to forgive your spouse?**

2. Are you afraid that there will be no protection for you if you let go of your resentments?

3. Are you stuck on your spouse making the first move because you feel that you are the one who does it all? How can you move beyond that?

4. Are you angry at God because of your spouse's sins? How?

5. For what do you need to ask your spouse to forgive you?

6. If you humble yourself before God and admit your own sinful behavior, how will God bless you?

7. Are you afraid of being taken advantage of if you get your heart right with God? How?

8. What do you think keeps Dee from not being able to trust and forgive John?

RECOVERY GUIDE

If your marriage is going to recover, you need to ask forgiveness from your spouse and from God. Repentance is the first step to take to rebuild trust. But once you have repented, you need to back up that repentance by being trustworthy, caring how your behavior affects your spouse and making amends when your actions damage the relationship. Only then will your broken relationship be mended.

Read Matthew 18:21–35.

1. How is forgiveness like releasing a debt?

2. What hurts and angry feelings are you still clinging to?

3. How is your relationship to God affected when you hold a grudge against someone?

4. How are you blocking good things from God when you don't forgive?

5. What gives you freedom to forgive your spouse?

Read Colossians 3:13.

1. What grievances do you have against your spouse?

2. What sins are you holding against your spouse?

3. To what degree are you commanded to forgive?

4. How is not following this command withholding from God?

5. In what ways will you express your forgiveness to your spouse?

6. In what ways will you bear with your spouse?

Read Luke 17:3–5.

1. This passage suggests that forgiveness is a response to repentance. What happens when you forgive but your spouse has not repented?

2. Is it possible or desirable to forgive your spouse silently, through prayer, without verbally forgiving him or her?

3. Do you have a difficult time being honest when your spouse sins against you?

4. Why are the apostles asking for more faith? Are they being humorous?

5. In what ways do you need more faith to forgive your spouse and repent from your sinful behavior?

RECOVERY GOALS

1. Are you willing to grow in maturity and let go of hurts and resentments in your heart?

2. Make a list of hurts or resentments that you are still carrying. Write them in a letter to God and end the letter with a prayer that asks God to cleanse your heart of these things. If you feel angry, be angry in the letter. If you feel hurt, be hurt in the letter and let it out. Healing takes time. You may need to repeat this process several times before you feel a release from your hurts. Make a choice to let go of these feelings and ask God to protect you from their power.

7. Restoring Balance and Rebuilding Trust

RECOVERY FOCUS

- Bring balance to your part in the relationship.
- Learn to view your relationship through your spouse's eyes.
- Earn your spouse's trust by making positive deposits in the relationship.

RECOVERY INFORMATION

Many Christians go to God for healing in their relationships, but often they do not go to the other person. To have complete reconciliation, however, both spouses must be involved. Relationships are not one-sided. They involve two people, and both need to do their part to heal a relationship. One of the chief characteristics of damaged marriages is that there is often a one-up, one-down dynamic: one spouse over-functions or does too much of the relational work, and one spouse under-functions and does too little of the relational work. A healthy relationship needs a balance, with both spouses functioning at a similar level.

Often the over-functioning spouse begins the reconciliation process. If you are an over-functioning spouse, you may have forgiven your spouse and released your angry feelings, and you may feel better. However, your relationship may not have changed. Since you have committed yourself to change, you attempt to be loving, but you feel stuck. You may feel guilty about the distance in your relationship, and you try harder to reconcile.

If you are an under-functioning spouse, you may feel angry and justify your distancing. You may feel powerless to do anything that will bring closeness or a sense of positive self-esteem. You say to yourself, Why try? You may tyrannize and wound your over-functioning spouse from this one-down position without realizing the damage you are doing. You may not believe you are powerful in the relationship.

Because you feel as if you are inadequate or the "bad guy," you may find it difficult to acknowledge your shortcomings. However, when you feel undergirded by God's love, acceptance, and forgiveness, you will feel safe in looking at your behavior without hating yourself. As you turn to God, you may begin to realize you have more power and may feel less victimized. You may be able to forgive and release your hurts and resentments. As you lessen your need to react, you may act in ways that build trust in the relationship.

John felt frustrated that he couldn't control Dee's distancing behavior. Out of this frustration he began to realize he needed to work on himself. John forgave Dee and tried to let go of the effects of her behavior, but he continued to react with old behavior patterns. He still felt victimized at times when Dee focused on the children or her mother.

John decided that he also must confess and surrender his resentment to God. As he prayed and asked God to help him see and feel his hidden resentments, he became aware how much his mother's critical, controlling attitude had affected him. John's mother had favored his older sister, and John felt he could do nothing right. His mother would manipulate him with guilt and shame. She often complained, "You're just like your father. You always have an excuse for everything."

Because he found he was no match for his mother, John had learned to withdraw from her. However, his withdrawing had set up a demand-and-withhold loop with his mother. As John worked through the spiritual dimensions of his resentments, he began to see how this resentment and rebellion with his mother was affecting his marriage.

John shared these insights with Dee and asked her to forgive him for justifying his withholding from her. He also asked her how his distancing had affected her. Dee began to cry as she told of feelings of frustration and abandonment. She shared how she would panic at times and not know where to go for emotional support. John then realized how her alliances with the children were substitute intimacies. He recognized how he had contributed to her unhealthy alliances.

Instead of resentment and blame, John felt he could do something about the distance in their relationship.

It was as if the air was clearing, and both felt a warmth and affection growing in their marriage. At times John was tempted to become defensive, but he had already come to realize that his behavior was wrong, even if he could justify it in his own mind. John decided that instead of seeing their marriage only through his own eyes, he would try to see the relationship through Dee's eyes and through the lens of Scripture.

Dee forgave John for his negative contributions in the relationship and how they had affected her. She felt she could begin to trust him again because he was willing to take responsibility for how he had affected her. John and Dee both said they were willing to start rebuilding trust and to earn it rather than demand it. Their reconciliation was coming together.

John found the rebuilding process difficult. He felt Dee was still resistant to his efforts to become close. He had to fight his fears and negative beliefs: "She'll never love me" or "She'll always be more interested in others." Because he contributed positively to the relationship, John felt he was entitled to some sexual closeness, and he felt hurt when Dee withheld. His temptation was to collect resentment, withdraw, and withhold from Dee. John fought this temptation and was honest with Dee when he felt rejected. She would talk with him, and their communication began opening up other areas in which they had felt stuck. Both John and Dee were willing to make positive deposits into their relationship and develop trust, even though it cost them to make these deposits.

EARNING TRUST

As we said in chapter 3, relationships are like bank accounts. When people act responsibly and dependably, they add to the account. They make deposits that cause the account to grow. However, when people hurt us or act irresponsibly, they take away from the account. They make withdrawals on the account. And if these withdrawals are made too often, the relationship becomes bankrupt.

If you have had too many relationships in which people withdrew from the accounts more than they deposited, you may find it difficult to trust. That was true for John. In his dysfunctional family John was the scapegoat. His mother picked on him, always wanting something from him. But she was never satisfied. If she didn't get what she wanted, she was critical and cruel to John. He felt life was unfair. He felt he was entitled to do wrong things and withhold doing right things.

When John didn't get what he wanted from Dee, he unconsciously punished her with meanness. Dee often felt victimized by John's behavior, and she felt he withdrew more from their emotional account than he deposited. As he depleted the emotional funds, Dee would ally with the children, further depleting the marriage's emotional account. John would then get angry, yell at the children, and take more from the marriage.

Through counseling, John realized how his withdrawals hurt his marriage relationship. He came to understand that in order to earn Dee's trust, he needed to make positive deposits into the relationship.

This was not easy for John. When Dee said no to him about a request, he had to fight the temptation to react and punish her. Instead, he needed to make a positive deposit into the account by giving her freedom and by showing kindness to her, even though she had said no to him. John felt afraid that Dee would take advantage of his kindness.

John's biggest fear centered on the secret sins he had committed over the frustration in his sex life. He had felt justified because of Dee's withholding and had rationalized his sexual misbehavior away until now. When he forgave Dee, he realized that his justification for the wrongs he had committed was gone. He was also now facing himself before God, and this was a difficult reality.

John struggled for days before he began to admit to himself that he had sinned against God, himself, and Dee. He felt tremendous grief over his shortcomings. In the midst of his grief, he found God reaching out to him with grace and forgiveness. He took comfort from the apostle Paul's statement that nothing can "separate us from the love of God that is in Christ Jesus our Lord" (Romans 8:35).

John no longer felt like the bad guy who was abandoned or beat up and punished. He felt forgiven and restored. As John meditated on Psalm 38 and Psalm 51, which tell of David's forgiveness and restoration, John felt healing in his soul. He was finally able to forgive himself, which also gave him more confidence in approaching Dee. When he became honest with God and himself, he was soon able to be more honest and intimate with Dee without feeling like the bad guy or the victim.

John began to make some positive deposits in his relationships. When he felt threatened, he would pray and contribute to the person threatening him. For example, instead of withdrawing if he saw Dee talking with the children, he would go over and join in the conversation. John was working very hard to make his account one that he could draw from without penalty on interest.

John was overcoming some of his negative beliefs. He was no longer under-functioning in the relationship. Instead of feeling entitled to his negative behavior, he was developing a new source of power or influence by doing what was right and good. He was now becoming an equal partner, changing his view of life and contributing in positive ways to the relationship. That doesn't mean he was becoming a carbon copy of Dee; it means he was giving up his negative reactions and allowing God to show him how he could make positive deposits into his marriage.

RECOVERY PROBERS

1. Do you over-function or under-function in your marriage?

2. How can you bring balance to your relationship?

3. In what areas of your relationship do you and your spouse need to build trust?

4. In what ways have you made withdrawals on the emotional account in your marriage?

5. Are you willing to hear your spouse talk about his or her hurts and resentments and not react, discount them, or minimize them? How can you express that willingness?

6. In what areas have you and your spouse been able to ask for forgiveness and talk about the effects of behaviors?

7. Do you tend to belabor a point and not let it go when talking about hurts and resentments?

8. Does belaboring a point punish the other person or offer forgiveness and grace?

9. How can you learn to see your relationship more from your spouse's frame of reference and God's perspective?

10. As you begin to rebuild trust, are you following through on the things you say you will do?

11. What behavior patterns undermine your credibility in building trust in your marriage?

RECOVERY GUIDE
Read 1 Peter 3:8–12.

1. What behaviors are you to stop?

2. What behaviors are you to start?

3. What is God's promise if you stop one behavior and begin another?

4. In what specific ways can you make this passage a part of your marriage relationship?

Read Micah 6:8.

1. In what ways will you act justly in your marriage?

2. In what ways will you be merciful with your spouse?

3. What does it mean to walk humbly with your God?

RECOVERY GOALS

1. In what specific areas do you need to make deposits in your marriage to build trust?

2. In what specific areas do you need to quit making withdrawals?

3. The emphasis in this chapter has been on reconciliation through both marriage partners doing their part in forgiving, repenting, and rebuilding trust. What do you need to do to help facilitate this process in your marriage relationship?

4. What steps will you take to *rebuild* trust?

5. What steps will you take to *earn* trust?

8.   Respect as a Cornerstone of Marriage

RECOVERY FOCUS

- Choose to value your spouse.
- Give your spouse freedom to say no.
- Respect your spouse's differences and weaknesses.

RECOVERY INFORMATION

One of the primary building blocks of a healthy marriage is respect. To respect your spouse is to acknowledge, value, and esteem him or her. In order to do that, you need to know your spouse. What does your spouse think, feel, and desire? Respect chooses to value what your spouse values. Respect is attentive to your spouse's needs and communicates that you value him or her as a separate entity, not just as an extension of you or your wishes.

Couples earn respect from each other. When you respect your spouse, that respect will often pay interest in your account and earn you respect in return. If you abuse your spouse's respect for you, you will lose it.

RESPECT AND HONOR

How do you treat people you respect? Do you make demands of them or manipulate them? Do you punish or belittle them if they don't do what you wish them to do? No! Naturally you would not treat those you respect that way. However, you may be doing these things to your spouse.

Respect offers freedom—the freedom to be yourself. It also offers safety and protection. One of the main manifestations of respect is that it gives a person the freedom to choose. Do you allow your spouse to say no to you? Is your spouse afraid to say no? Will your spouse feel punished if he or she says no? On the other hand, do you have the courage to say no in your relationship, or are you afraid of creating a conflict? Even though you may not say no, you may not really say yes either.

The Bible teaches that God created us with the freedom and ability to choose. We can say yes or no. We are not punished or devalued for our choices before God, but we are responsible for the consequences of these choices. The apostle John writes, "There is no fear in love. But perfect love drives out fear, because fear has to do with punishment. The one who fears is not made perfect in love" (1 John 4:18). How many times have you said no and then felt anxious about your spouse's distancing, pouting, or angry reactions?

Respect communicates the type of unconditional love that says, "I love *you*, not just what you can do for me." It works on eliminating the punitive elements in the relationship. Respect affirms the value of your spouse and the relationship. Respect allows your spouse to be honest and love from his or her heart. It says, "I want you to be real and honest in this relationship, and I give you the freedom to do that. I want you to do things because you want to do them, not just because I want them." You can be honest in saying, "I'm disappointed you don't want to spend time with me and the children, but I still love and value you." Respect shows concern for what your spouse thinks, feels, and desires.

Respect also includes *self-respect*. Self-respect means you value your own thoughts, feelings, and desires enough to share them with your spouse. Self-respect produces a paradox here in that it doesn't give freedom to behaviors that are self-destructive or ultimately destructive to the relationship, like infidelity, alcoholism, or even disrespectful behavior. Respect says, "I care about us enough not to ignore things that will harm us."

However, the honesty in confronting these destructive behaviors is still loving and respectful. Respect assumes you have the courage to define and assert your thoughts, feelings, and desires to your spouse. The goal here is mutual respect, both you and your spouse respect yourselves, each other, and your relationship.

One area of disrespect and dishonor in John and Dee's marriage was their sex life. As discussed earlier, they were stuck in a serious loop. John felt that Dee had no heart for him and felt this most directly when they were making love. She seemed disinterested. Dee felt John was not interested in her as a person and that he spent time with her only because he had to. Because of those feelings, it seemed unnatural for her to give herself to John sexually.

This is where the disrespect came into the relationship. For example, John would touch Dee in a sexual manner, and she would give him a look that poured cold water on any arousal he felt. He would say something like, "I'll be thankful when winter is over and things begin to thaw out around here." Dee would then become angry and hurt and would withdraw. John would feel hopeless about ever having sex with Dee and hesitant to initiate again.

John and Dee realized they were caught in a negative loop that not only left them frustrated but also made them act disrespectfully toward each other. They discussed their reactions to each other when John initiated a sexual expression. Because this was a sensitive issue for them, they knew they needed to communicate carefully. They were very honest about how they felt, but they saw the problem as one they needed to work on together. They were no longer enemies withholding happiness.

Dee said, "I feel as if it's not safe for me to be myself in this area. You punish me when I don't respond the way you want me to."

"How?" asked John incredulously.

"You pout and distance yourself from me, or you attack through sarcasm. I want to be able to say no and not be punished."

"I think I can do that, but I know I'll feel bad if I initiate and you don't respond," said John sheepishly.

Both decided that sexual interaction was an unsafe area and that they were afraid of each other's responses, so they set up some guidelines to help make it safer. For example, if John initiated closeness that would lead to having sex and Dee said no, then it was her responsibility to initiate closeness that led to sex within a couple of days. They made this decision because of Dee's tendency to withhold and distance in this area of their relationship.

This brought more balance to their sex life, but it caused a problem for Dee. She felt it was difficult for her to initiate sex when John was distant emotionally. They had to go back and discuss the guidelines.

"John, I agreed that if I said no to your sexual advances, I would be responsible to initiate sexual activity within a few days. And I want to do that. But I'm having trouble. It's hard for me to initiate sex with you when I don't feel emotionally close. If I feel distance, I'm not able to have sex. What can we do?"

"What would make you feel emotionally close? What would make you feel ready to have sex?"

"I need time to talk together, to share our feelings and thoughts. I need you to touch me at times when your agenda is not sexual intercourse. I can't come at sex 'cold' like you can."

"Well, don't we talk? Isn't that enough?" John replied, a bit confused.

"Sometimes when I initiate a time of closeness, like taking a walk together or just sitting with a cup of coffee to reflect about our day, you say no. You either want to read the paper or watch television, and I feel shut out. What if we apply the same guideline that we applied to your sexual needs to my need for emotional closeness? If I initiate time together for emotional closeness, you are free to say no. But then I'd like you to create some emotional closeness within the next few days. That way I can give you the freedom to say no, but I know you'll respect my need and work to meet it within a short period of time."

Both made commitments to initiate love the way the other one desired to be loved. They made each other's feelings important. Dee felt loved when John showed interest in her emotionally. John felt loved when Dee was affectionate, warm, and sexual. The relationship became safer for both Dee and John as they began to cut out their disrespectful comments and deal with their disappointments more maturely. They were also making a commitment to care about how they were affecting each other and making each other's thoughts, feelings, and desires important. There was now a different tone to the relationship, a new spirit of respect that made the relationship safer for both. This, in turn, made the relationship more enjoyable and brought back some warmth.

RESPECTING DIFFERENCES AND WEAKNESSES

In a healthy marriage, couples value their differences and view them as being a complement to the marriage. However in an unhealthy marriage, the couple is threatened and reacts to differences. If one is outgoing, the other must be outgoing. If one is sensitive, the other must be sensitive. If one is assertive, the other is not allowed to be shy.

How do you feel when your spouse sees an issue differently from how you see it? Do you feel yours is the right perspective? Do you discount or minimize your spouse's view, or do you give value to the viewpoint even if you don't agree?

Some people enjoy the differences between them before they marry, but once they get into the marriage, the differences become a source of serious conflict. Before he married Dee, John liked her ability to be nurturing. But later he resented her nurturing of the children and saw her as permissive. Before Dee married John, she admired his success and competence at work. But later she saw his competence and success as workaholism.

In an unhealthy marriage, couples empower each other's weaknesses. They react to weaknesses instead of allowing space or working out the problem. In a healthy marriage, couples respect their differences and try to work through them so that differences can become strengths. Respect can turn a weakness into a strength through giving each other honor or affirmation.

One night John brought home flowers and gave them to Dee. She asked, "What are these for?"

John replied, "I just wanted to say that I am glad you are the mother of my children." Dee said in counseling that she felt that little bit of affirmation for six weeks. Respect produces responsiveness and affirmation.

Respecting each other's weaknesses is also very important in producing trust in a marriage relationship. When spouses are insensitive about the other's weaknesses, the relationship becomes unsafe again. Couples show disrespect for each other's weaknesses when they parade those weaknesses in front of other people. Have you fallen into that trap? Do you play the blemish game with your spouse, making sure your spouse sees his or her faults? Do you discuss your spouse's faults in front of others?

When you or your spouse shares something intimate, you need to respect your spouse's vulnerability and protect him or her. If you disrespect your spouse by mistreating that information or criticizing your spouse for what he or she has shared, then you may lose closeness.

John's counselor told him to start sharing his thoughts, feelings, and desires with Dee through keeping a journal. As John shared things from his journal with Dee, he often found her criticizing or trying to fix him. John would feel as if he never wanted to share again. He then would say, "Dee, please don't criticize me or try to fix me. Just listen and let me share myself." It took a while for Dee to respect his wishes, and it took perseverance for John to continue to open up.

Once Dee shared some of John's journal with her friend. When John found out through the friend's husband, he was wounded. Dee apologized and made a commitment to be more private with their secrets, and John opened up again.

John also had to work at showing respect for Dee's weaknesses. Dee disliked her older sister and tried very hard not to be like her. However, in many ways she was just like her. Knowing this was one of her weaknesses, John would capitalize on it. Every time John pointed out that she was acting or thinking like her sister, he would crush Dee. John set a boundary on his cutting comments and quit comparing Dee to her sister. He then began to recognize Dee's effort to be different, and Dee felt as if John was her ally.

Respecting your spouse's weaknesses builds trust and enables you to be close.

RECOVERY PROBERS

1. In what ways do you show disrespect for your spouse?

2. How would your spouse say you show disrespect for him or her?

3. How do you show you value your spouse?

4. How would your spouse say you value him or her?

5. What do you value most about your relationship?

6. What would your spouse say he or she values most about your relationship?

7. In what area is it most difficult for you to give your spouse freedom to say no to you? Does your spouse know this?

8. In what area is it most difficult for you to say no? Why? Does your spouse know this?

9. Do you show respect or disrespect for your spouse's differences? Explain with specific examples.

10. Which difference is hardest for you to handle?

11. What steps can you take to begin to respect your spouse's differences?

12. In what area would your spouse say you are the most affirming?

RECOVERY GUIDE

Read Ephesians 5:33.

1. What difference does it make to you that the Bible asks you to love, honor, and respect your spouse?

2. Where do you fall short on this command? Where do you do well?

Read 2 Corinthians 5:16—17.

1. Part of respect is believing the best about your spouse rather than focusing on his or her weaknesses. Is it difficult for you to see the "new" part of your spouse?

2. How do you empower your spouse's weaknesses (the old part) by reacting to them?

3. How can you learn to see Christ in your spouse?

4. What happens to you when someone believes the best in you?

Read John 3:16.

1. If God values you enough to allow his only Son to die for you, how does that give you strength to value your spouse?

2. How does your view of your spouse change when you choose to see him or her through God's eyes?

3. How does this verse help you respect your spouse's differences?

RECOVERY GOALS

1. In what area of your relationship do you have a difficult time respecting your spouse?

2. Have you talked about this with your spouse?

3. Are you willing to change and work toward mutual respect? When?

4. Ask your spouse to discuss this issue with you. Evaluate together where each of you needs to respect the other. Ask how you could earn more respect from your spouse. Set up goals that are realistic and gracious. Make sure you reevaluate your goals periodically to make sure each spouse's needs are met.

5. How will you work together and develop respect in your relationship?

9.   Dialogues of Give and Take

RECOVERY FOCUS

- Learn how to have balanced dialogues with your spouse.
- Learn to listen for the message being sent.
- Make your dialogues safe for your spouse.

RECOVERY INFORMATION

Have you ever felt as if no matter how hard you try, you can't get your spouse to hear you? At other times you are able to peel through all the shallow levels of interaction and achieve meaningful communication with your spouse. Those times of connection build your account and are invaluable.

A key to a healthy marriage is a couple's ability to have dialogues. Much of the communication in struggling marriages is like two monologues, with each person talking *at* the other rather than *with* one another.

DIALOGUE VERSUS MONOLOGUE

When couples engage in simultaneous monologues, their goal is to defend themselves and justify their own ideas rather than to listen and be responsive. They are trying to make the other understand rather than have an *exchange* of understanding.

Dialogue is a two-way communication. Couples who engage in dialogue want to understand each other more than they want to be understood. They know the importance of listening and asking questions. They know the balance of listening and speaking. Sometimes to earn the right to be understood, you have to work on being understanding.

For a dialogue to work, it must set people free from binds in the relationship rather than create new bad feelings. A good dialogue creates an energy between two people that brings a deeper relation-

71

ship. It makes you feel better instead of worse. Dialoguing is a skill that can be developed, but it takes work like any other skill.

Often your level of stress is one of the key factors that defines your ability to communicate. When you are stressed out, anxious, or tired, you don't have the energy to talk things through, so you react. You revert to old patterns of anger or frustration, fear or sadness. You disguise these emotions in words, and you find your spouse often misses the message and reacts to the words. That was the case with John and Dee.

John walked in the door and blurted out, "My boss yells at me every day. I'd like to quit."

Dee, without thinking, reacted to the content of the words. Dee said, "John, your boss doesn't yell at you every day, and you can't quit. Don't feel that way."

Wham! Dee created a negative loop. In listening only to John's words, she missed the more important emotional message: "I'm frustrated and discouraged." She shut John down by not giving him the freedom to express his feelings.

What happened to John's feelings when Dee responded this way? He later told her, "Your comments only frustrated me further. I don't need you to judge me, to tell me I'm right or wrong. I need you to hear me and respond to my feelings."

What could Dee have said? If she had been able to acknowledge the emotion and respond to it, the dialogue may have sounded like this:

Dee: "John, you look and sound beat up."

John: "I'm just tired of everything going wrong at work."

Dee: "Do you want to tell me what it was today?"

John: (Looking at Dee) "He was second guessing me again on that project I've been working on. It drives me nuts, like I can't do anything right. Plus, he seems to criticize me and mistrust my judgment."

Dee: "No space or respect."

John: "Yeah, that's it. That's exactly how I feel, like he is crowding me. It's my project, and he is being disrespectful of that."

Dee: "I'd be frustrated too if someone was standing over my shoulder."

John: (With confidence) "I think I'm going to tell him how I feel. What do you think about me doing that, Dee?"

Dee: "Well, that would probably help. Has he been this controlling in the past?"

John: "No, not really. Maybe something is eating him. I'll ask what is up with him."

In this dialogue, Dee didn't react to John's words or give advice. She made a connection with John rather than creating a break with him.

Do you recognize and acknowledge feelings in your spouse when you listen to him or her? Do you respect these feelings when you hear them? A healthy dialogue is built on respect and trust. Disbelieving or second-guessing is disrespectful. "No, that's not what you really mean!" only provokes reactivity.

Are you respecting your spouse and yourself when you communicate? Are you showing your spouse that you care and are willing to make him or her important in your life? Are you honest and direct, willing to take risks in your communication?

If you haven't taken a class or read a book about communication skills, consider doing that. We recommend *Telling Each Other the Truth* by William Backus. You can learn to have a constructive dialogue. Learn to listen for the thoughts, feelings, and desires expressed in your spouse's words. Then respond to those thoughts or feelings. Or ask questions that will help your spouse understand himself or herself better.

SAFETY AND ENJOYMENT

It is your responsibility to make your dialogues as safe and enjoyable as possible. No one else is going to do that for you. Even the strongest people are vulnerable emotionally with their spouses and will retreat or attack when a dialogue becomes unsafe or painful. It is important that you also take responsibility for how you receive things from your spouse. If you tend to internalize or take things personally when they are not intended that way, that may be your issue rather than your spouse's insensitivity.

John often felt threatened by Dee and would respond defensively. Dee felt as if she were walking on eggs at times because John was so "touchy." No matter how she tried to make the conversation safe, John still seemed to react.

At first, Dee felt this was her fault. If she could just be perfect, he would not react. Dee would internalize John's anger and feel guilty. She would also collect hurts, blocking a free-flowing dialogue. She would feel overly responsible and become defensive. However, she was beginning to take responsibility for her over-functioning as her awareness of the problem increased.

John discovered that he was dragging some of his negative behavior patterns from his past into his relationship with Dee. He realized he needed to be less on guard and more trusting of Dee's love for him.

An area that was unsafe for both John and Dee was their finances. John had started a small business on the side, and it had failed, leaving them with considerable debt. Dee felt in a bind over this because John would overreact when she brought up the subject of finances and cut her off. Yet, she was affected daily by this large debt. She felt stuck, and so did John. Neither of them saw any other options.

Dee would feel distanced and cut off whenever she brought up the subject. She didn't know how to begin a dialogue that would not touch John off. John felt Dee pressured him to talk about something that only made him feel guilty and helpless to fix. How could they make this a safe subject for them when they were both emotionally raw in this area? The following is an example of a dialogue that had some give and take for both of them and produced a win-win situation.

Dee said to John, "The bank called me today and said we are overdrawn on our account again."

"I'm sick of this stuff with this debt," said John in disgust.

Dee asserts herself, "John, I'm not attacking you. I'm just tired of being hassled by the bank over this bad debt and what it's doing to us." She attempts to stay on same team.

"Dee, there isn't anything I can do, and it upsets me to talk about it," says John.

"John, I won't talk about it if you don't want me to. I'd like you just to listen to me and give me a little emotional support after fighting with the bank. Would you?" Dee shows respect and makes a request.

"I don't see what good it will do to talk about it. It won't change the fact we are in debt, will it?"

"No, it won't. But I would feel better if I could tell you how I feel when things happen, like the bank calling me." Dee shows courage by asking again.

"Well, I usually feel blamed and guilty when you share your frustrations over our finances," says John, sharing his feelings.

"You aren't sure you can handle me sharing my feelings without you feeling bad. Is there anything I can do to make this safer for you besides not sharing?" Dee listens for feelings and shows concern.

"You can leave the big stick with the nail in it in the closet when you share," John says with a smile, hoping to break the tension with humor.

Dee laughs and smiles at John and says, "Well, can I just use a rubber hose then and beat you a little? I guess the tension of picking up the phone and not knowing if I'm going to be attacked by an angry creditor is what upsets me," Dee continues.

"Dee, I know you feel as if this debt and its consequences have caused you to feel unprotected and unsafe."

"John, that's right. I just want to be able to say that to you sometimes when it's getting to me. Thanks for hearing me."

"Sure."

RECOVERY PROBERS

1. When you listen, does your spouse feel you are interested and attentive?

2. When you listen, what is most difficult for you to hear and be responsive to: thoughts, feelings, or desires?

3. In a dialogue are you better at talking or listening?

4. In a dialogue that has tension in it, are you able to be reasonable, responsible, and respectful? Do you tend to be demanding and give advice, telling your spouse how he or she should respond or fix the problem? Or do you make excuses, feeling weak or helpless, or are you defensive? Ask others for feedback.

5. When you have a discussion with your spouse, are you able to continue interacting when the flow of conversation begins to hit resistance? If not, what stops you? If yes, what gives you courage and strength to continue?

6. Do you feel safe even when you disagree or don't get what you want?

7. Do your dialogues help you resolve the conflict, help you feel better, or make life more manageable? If not, what can you do to enhance your dialogues?

RECOVERY GUIDE

Read James 1:19–20.

1. Is it difficult for you to listen to your spouse? What compulsive feelings do you have when listening?

2. Can you force a person to hear you by being loud or angry?

3. How will you practice listening to your spouse?

4. What sin in this area do you need to confess?

Read Philippians 2:3–5.

1. When you are engaged in dialogue, do you demonstrate that you are interested in your spouse's interests? How?

2. Does this passage say you are not to have interests of your own?

3. How did Christ demonstrate that others were important?

4. How do you show selfish ambition or vain conceit to your spouse?

Read Proverbs 13:10.
1. Pride often presumes to know everything and therefore blocks true listening and understanding. How does your pride keep you from understanding your spouse?

2. How will you practice humility in your dialogues with your spouse?

RECOVERY GOALS
1. As you work together to strengthen your ability to communicate, remember these principles:
   - Be specific and positive rather than vague and negative.
   - Take responsibility for your personal issues and stay away from generalizing and philosophizing.
   - Be direct and to the point, but do not belabor the issue or use your emotions as a weapon.
   - Use words that validate rather than words that discount your spouse.
   - Be open and vulnerable. Listen to criticism without being defensive, but don't be disrespectful to yourself.

2. Write out a specific comment or conversation you could have with your spouse demonstrating the first principle: Be specific and positive rather than vague and negative.

3. Write out a specific comment or conversation you could have with your spouse demonstrating the second principle: Take responsibility for your personal issues and stay away from generalizing and philosophizing.

4. Write out a specific comment or conversation you could have with your spouse demonstrating the third principle: Be direct and to the point, but do not belabor the issue or use your emotions as a weapon.

5. Write out a specific comment or conversation you could have with your spouse demonstrating the fourth principle: Use words that validate rather than words that discount your spouse.

6. Write out a specific comment or conversation you could have with your spouse demonstrating the fifth principle: Be open and vulnerable. Listen to criticism without being defensive, but don't be disrespectful to yourself.

10. Contracts That Build Marriages

RECOVERY FOCUS

- Develop realistic expectations of your spouse.
- Define your expectations of the relationship in a clear contract.
- Look to God for strength to continue to grow.

RECOVERY INFORMATION

When your expectations of your spouse are not realistic, destructive things can happen. When your spouse fails to live up to your expectations, you may become disappointed, disillusioned, embittered, or alienated.

You can eliminate some of this stress and frustration by making a contract with your spouse, a clear agreement in which you realistically define and agree on your expectations of yourselves, each other, and your relationship. A contract allows your relationship to become more predictable and dependable.

Clear contracts require two ingredients: the courage to be honest in the dialogue and the character or maturity to carry out your commitments. Honesty and maturity give your relationship security and safety. Relationships without honesty and maturity lapse into chaos and reactivity, both of which rob a relationship of safety.

FORM AND FREEDOM IN MARRIAGE

Does having a contract or agreement mean you give up your freedom to be yourself? What can you realistically expect from your spouse? Do you expect your spouse to change into someone he or she is not? Do you expect your spouse to be perfect? Are you making your happiness dependent on your spouse changing? Are you looking for a quick fix rather than a steady process of growth? Are you willing to change? Are you looking to get from your spouse what you didn't get from your parents? Are your dreams and hopes for your marriage realistic? All these questions can help you define whether you are developing a healthy marriage contract.

One of the quickest ways to become miserable is to have unrealistic expectations. We develop unrealistic expectations when we do not have a connection or a commitment from our spouse. Maybe you are like many spouses. You drop hints and make suggestions to your spouse about your expectations, and you think that's enough to achieve the desired change. You expect your spouse to read between the lines and hear the nuances in your hints. What you perceive as "making your needs known" adds up to little more than "wishful thinking."

That's where contracts can be helpful. Contracts or agreements help couples define their commitments and expectations. This contract can assist in providing a structure that gives the relationship a sense of security and dependability.

In relationships that are relatively healthy, these agreements are casual and flexible in most areas because of the relaxed atmosphere in the marriage. In more tense relationships, agreements must be more specific, but not rigid.

You need to define the what, where, when, and how—without creating more tension. Be careful to maintain freedom in respecting your spouse's choices and honest responses. The life of the relationship may be lost without balancing this need for freedom. Relationships need both security and freedom to thrive.

It takes work and communication to develop workable contracts. For example, John asked Dee if she would pay the monthly bills. Dee agreed to try. John began to get nervous and frustrated as the due date for the bills approached. Did John have a contract with Dee to pay the bills? If he did, what could he expect? Was Dee honest with John? Was John's expectation of Dee taking over the bills realistic?

Finally, John blew up at Dee because she didn't pay the bills when he expected her to.

Dee: (Defensive) "I did as many of them as I could."
John: "They *all* must be paid on time."
Dee: "I thought I was just going to *help* you pay the bills. You've always done them before."
John: "You said you would pay the bills."
Dee: "I said I'd *try*, which meant I'd get to them if I had time."

John: (Stopping the reacting, he breathed deeply.) "I guess I wasn't clear on what I was expecting from you."

Dee: "And I wasn't clear on my commitment to you."

John: "What I want from you, Dee, is to have all the bills paid by their due dates. Are you willing to do that?"

Dee: "John, I'm very busy, and I'm not sure I can get all the bills paid. I would like to split them with you rather than take on the whole load."

John: (Looking very contemplative) "Some bills can be paid on the first of every month, and others must be paid on the fifteenth. I would prefer to do the ones on the fifteenth."

Dee: (Feeling some resolve to their tension) "That would be fine with me."

John: "So I can count on you getting your share of the bills paid by the first of each month?"

Dee: "Yes, I'll be glad to do that."

This contract balanced the burden of the work load for John, and he felt thankful that Dee was willing to carry more of this burden. Did Dee have the freedom to say how she felt about the bills? Did John care how she felt, and was he willing to respect her? Do they now have a contract that will bring some security and freedom to their relationship? To have a realistic contract both people need to look at and discuss their limitations realistically.

Note how both form and freedom are needed in the relationship. The form, the contract or agreement, protects you from unrealistic expectations and disappointment. This prevents you from sliding into negative reactions or demanding behavior and encourages respect for each other. The freedom makes you more likely to be honest and less likely to withhold from your spouse. Learning how to define a contract with a spouse can help the relationship mature and stabilize. This is part of creating and maintaining positive loops of trust and respect.

Contracts help balance the burden and blessings of the relationship. Contracts can be as little or unimportant as deciding who takes out the trash or as significant as fidelity in marriage. When the expectation of not taking out the trash is broken, it may bring some minor frustrations, but infidelity may cause the marriage to end in divorce.

FINDING STRENGTH IN GOD

John and Dee found that making their relationship healthy was hard work. Sometimes they lost perspective and felt they had no options. They would lapse into black-and-white thinking, thereby eliminating creative problem solving and leaving them with the old win-lose power struggle. Other times they lapsed into immaturity and forgot their personal limitations. This kept them shortsighted and inhibited their ability to be reasonable. When they became anxious, they could see only their own side of the issue.

John and Dee also overlooked the fact that building a good marriage and a workable marriage contract takes a lifetime. Often Dee would feel that if their conflicts led to an impasse again, all their counseling was in vain and the marriage was not going to make it. John was more relaxed but would also feel discouraged when they had conflicts and setbacks, which their counselor described as a normal part of life.

Gradually John and Dee realized that if their marriage was to survive, they needed to depend much more on God. Their old patterns did not involve a commitment to discover and follow God's will. As they moved toward wholeness, they began to crave direction and strength from God.

As they learned to turn more to God, they were able to talk about what each of them wanted in a situation. They could then creatively work toward a contract that considered both of their needs. Without this spiritual component, it was difficult to compromise and work out expectations. When they included God, they were able to negotiate and compromise, rather than enter into a power struggle.

John and Dee began to find that when they stayed out of the reactionary loops and engaged in honest dialogue, they often both got what they wanted. They wanted to respect each other's desires but at times felt helpless without God's support. The relationship was becoming more of a win-win situation with this spiritual side included. This was usually a result of each of them turning to God, admitting their powerlessness and having him deal with their hearts. This meant at times Dee would have to wait on God rather than pursue John for a resolution. Other times, John needed to be obedient to God and be a giver rather than a withholder.

As they began to grow spiritually in their marriage, they would discuss and pray about a matter and come up with creative solutions. Sometimes it was months before a resolution was brought about by God working in their relationship, but as they felt more secure, they could wait. The Lord was empowering them. They also became much more imaginative in getting their needs met in healthy and godly ways. Their energy level was higher as they gained hope that God would work to bring about a fulfillment of their expectations in his timing and his way.

RECOVERY PROBERS

1. What unrealistic expectations does your spouse have of you?

2. What unrealistic expectations do you have of your spouse?

3. How do you react when your spouse doesn't meet your expectations?

4. How can you tell when your spouse's commitment isn't dependable?

5. Are your contracts flexible enough to allow for change? How?

6. How do you bring negotiation and compromise into your dialogues about expectations?

7. What do you do when you feel as if you have no options and your relationship is sliding back into a win-lose situation?

8. Do your conversations about your contracts produce creative thinking and keep you on the same team or do they produce resistance and alienation?

9. How can God strengthen you as you build your relationship?

10. How can you learn to become more dependent on God's leading in your relationship?

RECOVERY GUIDE

Read Psalm 127:1.

1. What is the main point of this passage?

2. How is God involved in building your marriage?

3. Paraphrase this verse, using your marriage and your names in place of the other words in the verse.

Read Galatians 5:4–6.

God's Old Testament contract or covenant with the nation of Israel was a conditional contract. If Israel obeyed, God blessed them, and if they disobeyed, God cursed them (Leviticus 26). However, God promised a new covenant that was unconditional, based on the work of God in our hearts (Jeremiah 31:31–34). In this new covenant God works through the power of his Spirit rather than the letter of his Law.

1. Do you believe your marriage is under the new or the old covenant?

2. Do you love your spouse unconditionally? Does your spouse feel secure in that love?

3. Would your spouse say your marriage is unconditional or conditional in the contract? How?

4. Are you being led by God's Spirit or by your own strength in your marriage?

5. Is your hope for creating a good marriage in God's Spirit or in your spouse or yourself?

Read Matthew 5:37.

1. Are you clear in the commitments you make?

2. How does this passage relate to making contracts with your spouse?

3. Do others know when you say no?

4. When you say yes or no to something, are you serious about following through on what you say you will or will not do?

RECOVERY GOALS

1. Describe a simple agreement or contract—like the one John and Dee made for paying the bills—you will try to make with your spouse, and follow through on this agreement.

2. In what areas are you still experiencing frustration or disappointment over unfulfilled expectations?

3. Are your expectations realistic in this area?

4. Does your spouse know of your expectations?

5. What is your part of the contract?

6. Is God requiring anything from you in this area before you can move forward?

7. Make a commitment to work through this process to eliminate impasses in your marriage relationship. Building a good marriage is a process of growth that can be rewarding on a daily basis, but it takes a lifetime to complete. Remember that you must live one day at a time.

LEADER'S GUIDE

WORKING WITH PEOPLE RECOVERING FROM DAMAGED MARRIAGES

If you would like to lead a recovery group for couples, you need to make sure you are capable of maintaining control of the group. Explosive marriages can upset others, causing them to lose hope instead of encouraging healing and recovery. If a couple is too explosive, they should first do some marriage counseling. As they gain stability, they will be able to use the group to further their recovery. Screen your couples carefully before you start a group and work with those who have some stability or are on the road to recovery.

I am not saying that expressions of emotion and conflict should not be a part of this group; they should. However, the leader needs to be comfortable with conflict and capable of bringing some resolution to the process. The group should not turn into another place where a couple fights to an impasse.

Be careful of group members forming alliances with other members over issues that are similar to their own. For example, Kathy and Sue both have husbands who have cheated on them, and they ally together and put down men. These alliances keep members from owning their parts in the relationship and allow the reactive loops to continue.

This group may need stronger leadership than some of the other recovery groups. If you are a passive leader, this may not be a group that you will lead easily.

PURPOSE OF GROUP

Involve people in defining this purpose so that they have some personal ownership in the group dynamic and can define some of their personal goals.

1. To provide people with the hope of recovery from damaged marriages
2. To give information about damaged marriages and how they can be rebuilt
3. To show that problems are universal
4. To provide a place to work on damaged marriage relationships
5. To provide practical steps for healing

GROUP FORMAT

Suggested size of group: 8–12 members.

Suggested length of time for the group: 12–15 weeks, spending 1–2 hours per session. Highly motivated groups can be engaged for a longer period of time. To really learn the material, a group may need to stay together for twenty to thirty weeks and take two to three weeks to work through a chapter. This material works well as follow-up material for couples who have worked the *Codependency Confusion* workbook.

Opening Sessions

1. Define the purposes of the group and ask why people are there.
2. Read together the Group Ground Rules, found on the following pages.
3. Ask each person to take 10–15 minutes to give his or her personal background and tell his or her story.
4. Define your expectations of attendance and workbook involvement. Get clear commitments from group members.
5. Establish a support network for the group members. Talk about meeting outside the group for coffee, exchange phone numbers, and the like.

Workbook Sessions

1. Open each session with prayer, asking for God's presence to protect and lead the group.
2. Share victories, especially those related to previous chapters. Encourage people to share goals they have met.
3. Discuss the various sections of the week's workbook chapter, asking questions about the Recovery Information and using the questions in the Recovery Probers and Recovery Guide for group discussion.
6. Share current struggles. Allow people time to work on struggles.
7. Pray together each week.
8. If you feel comfortable, involve the group in role playing and practicing dialogues. Come with a prepared situation you want them to role play or talk about, or give the group freedom to practice on situations from their own marriage.

Closing Sessions

1. Focus on what has been gained by reflecting on victories.
2. Talk about what relationships have been meaningful.
3. Make a commitment to have a reunion in three months.
4. Talk about where people can now find support.

GROUP GROUND RULES

1. All conversations in this group are confidential and may not be shared with anyone outside the group. If permission is asked and everyone is comfortable, an exception can be made. Protection leading to trust building is a goal of this group.
2. These groups aren't open groups, which means that others can't be invited after the group starts. There can be exceptions if the group and the group leader agree.
3. It is important that people share what they are experiencing and that they don't generalize. They need to own their own feelings and not judge others. For example, say "I resent my husband's insensitivity to my needs" instead of "Husbands can't be romantic."
4. Members aren't responsible for other members; group members are not responsible to give advice, excuse other people's actions, or fix hurting people. What this means is there is no cross-talk allowed. Group members may share experiences from their point of view if someone in the group needs that information.
5. Listen without interrupting, unless you are the leader and responsible to watch the time in sharing. Each person's story and experience is valuable. Each group member is valuable.
6. Avoid using "shoulds" or "oughts" in the group, either for yourself or others.
7. If a group member becomes anxious about the group experience, talk about it in the group. If a group member wants to quit the group over fearful feelings or resentment, talk about it in the group. Do a reality check with the person, helping him or her to see if the fear is warranted or just a part of the recovery process. Honesty is a key to successful recovery. And honesty can be practiced at times like this in the group.
8. Stay on the goals and purposes of the group and keep conversations directed.
9. Make and express additional ground rules that would make this group a more effective place for recovery to occur.

10. If a couple (or individual) is too volatile, too disruptive, or creates too much conflict in the group, refer them to marriage counseling until they can manage their reactions in a group setting.

GROUP PROCESS

Groups form in stages. The initial stage is one of bonding, a stage in which group members share about themselves and find out if the group is safe. The leader's role is to facilitate safety and openness. Leaders need to work toward giving everyone the opportunity to share. Be careful not to allow group members to try to rescue each other or form unhealthy alliances (as in the case of women against men).

In later stages, the group members will jockey for positions. Don't be surprised if group members challenge your leadership and some members re-create in the group the dysfunctional behavior that led to their damaged marriages. Your role is to avoid thinking like a victim or rescuer and to move the group and its members toward personal responsibility, godliness, and healthy thinking. This gives opportunity for real dialogue between group members and for teaching of new skills.

In the last stages, the group needs to learn to let go and say good-bye in a healthy way. Help the group to focus on what they have learned and how they have grown. Help group members reflect on their victories and express their joy from relationships. Your role will be one of helping members not to rationalize but to face their feelings and to understand how their attitudes and behavior affect their spouses.

REFERRALS

Couples who are too volatile should be referred to a marriage counselor. If a couple is talking about divorce, you should refer them to a pastor or counselor. This is not a therapy group but a recovery group, so referrals are an important part of accepting our limitations as leaders.

Couples going through marriage crises often experience depression, grief, and high levels of anxiety. Any signs of deep depression such as insomnia, significant weight loss or weight gain, withdrawal from life tasks, or suicidal thoughts signal problems that are too serious to be handled in a support group. Refer people with these signs to a pastor, counseling professional, or hospital. Other issues may arise that would call for referrals. When developing a referral list, consider:

1. Caring churches that minister to people
2. Treatment centers
3. Christian counselors
4. Social service agencies

SUGGESTED QUALIFICATIONS FOR GROUP LEADERS

For maximum effectiveness, leaders will have

1. achieved and maintained some stability in their own marriage.
2. been a Christian for several years and have a basic knowledge of the Bible.
3. a dynamic relationship to Christ and a commitment to pray daily for their group members.
4. experience in facilitating a group. If possible, leaders will first serve as co-leaders of a group before having primary leadership responsibilities.
5. experience teaching and practicing basic communication skills, like "using 'I messages,'" "reflective listening," "problem ownership," "setting boundaries" and the like.
6. accountability to the leaders of the facility in which the support group meets. For instance, if the group meets in a church and is sanctioned by the church, support-group leaders will be accountable to the church's leadership.
7. wisdom on knowing when to refer group members for professional help.
8. Christ-centered motives for leading a group.
9. no anxiety about strong expressions of emotion.
10. demonstrated diligence in working through his or her own marriage-crises issues.

SUGGESTED READINGS

If you found this Recovery Discovery workbook helpful, you may also find help from the following books:

Augsberger, David. *Caring Enough to Forgive, Caring Enough Not to Forgive.* Venture, Calif.: Regal, 1980.

Brandt, Henry, with Phil Landrum. *I Want My Marriage to Be Better.* Grand Rapids: Zondervan, 1976.

Conway, Jim and Sally. *Traits of a Lasting Marriage.* Downers Grove, Ill.: InterVarsity Press, 1991.

Crabb, Larry. *Marriage Builder, with Discussion Guide.* Grand Rapids: Zondervan, 1992.

Dobson, James. *What Wives Wish Their Husbands Knew About Women.* Wheaton, Ill.: Tyndale House, 1975.

Jenkins, Jerry B. *Hedges: Loving Your Marriage Enough to Protect It.* Brentwood, Tenn.: Wolgemuth and Hyatt, 1989.

Lerner, Harriet Goldhor. *The Dance of Anger.* San Francisco: Harper & Row, 1989.

Mason, Mike. *The Mystery of Marriage.* Portland, Ore.: Multnomah Press, 1985.

Smalley, Gary, with Steve Scott. *For Better or for Best.* Grand Rapids: Zondervan, 1979.

Smalley, Gary. *If Only He Knew.* Grand Rapids: Zondervan, 1979.

Osborne, Cecil G. *The Art of Understanding Your Mate.* Grand Rapids: Zondervan, 1970.

Williams, Jill and Pat. *Rekindled.* Old Tappan,. N.J.: Revell, 1985.